The Ballad of Sid Kipper

Chris Sugden and Sid Kipper

Credit and thanks are due to Dick Nudds, who had a hand in certain parts of this book.

We are grateful to all the photographers who have given permission for their work to be used in this book: Coote Memorial Museum (pp. 3, 4, 9, 23 and 65); Graham Pirt (p. 6); Maggie Hunt (p. 7); Clive Tully (p. 11); Ron Hill (p. 16); Dripping Tap Productions (p. 32); Tom Glancy (p. 86). We are also grateful to those we could not trace and assume we have their tacit permission.

Published in 1996 by Mousehold Press,
Victoria Cottage, Constitution Opening,
Norwich, NR3 4BD

Cover design by Patrick Loan

ISBN 1 874739 06 4

Printed by Watkiss Studios Ltd., Biggleswade

The Ballad of Sid Kipper

This book is dedicated to my father, Len Sugden, as a small gesture of love and esteem.

CONTENTS

FOREWORD – THE WRITTEN KIPPER

I first met Sid Kipper eighteen months ago in the barn of our small farm. I was plucking a pheasant and he was wanting some more feathers for his pillow. I was immediately struck by his intellect, sense of vision and the five pounds fluttering from his left hand. Later, I heard him sing and realised that here was a man of extraordinary talent. Not only was he a member of one of Britain's most endangered species – a countryman – but he was also possibly the last of the country's wandering minstrels.

Now, at last, Sid has produced this remarkable book – part autobiography, part complete fiction, part songbook and part invaluable reference book. Some of his writing is like pure poetry and once picked up I found it difficult to put down – I had spilt marmalade on the cover.

It gave me many chuckles, smiles and – something that is extremely difficult for someone of my delicate, slim disposition – belly laughs. 'How the Turkey Got His Gobble', 'The Wraggle-Taggle Travellers', 'Old, Waily, Windy Knight' are all mini classics and there are many more.

Sid Kipper is a very funny man and this is a very funny book. Laughter is good for our health and so is Sid Kipper. But, although funny, there are shafts of real insight and sanity in this excellent volume. Sid cares about the countryside and those of us who still live in it. He has the eye of a conservationist and the wit of a traditional stand-up comic – a wonderful combination.

Read this book and give one to a friend.

Robin Page

VERSE ONE – THE MAN

In which we meet the hero of the ballad, hear of his doings,
and persuade him to put them away.

Of all the lays a singer laid,
The sounds that all were sounded;
Of all the strains that were ever strained,
The rounds that all were rounded;
Of all the airs that e'er were aired,
The croons that all got crooned;
Of all the catches ever caught,
The tunes that once were tuned;
There's none of them shall ever beat,
There's none shall be the whipper,
Of that great burden, here put down,
The Ballad of Sid Kipper.

A Star is Spawned

Sid Kipper was born on a sunny Saturday afternoon in Farmer Trout's barn in the tiny Norfolk village of St Just-near-Trunch, which means that Sid is a true Truncheon (and he never has to close the door). Many people have remarked that Sid seems younger than his age. Well, every biography needs a sensational revelation, so here's one straight away: I can now exclusively divulge that Sid *is* younger than his age! That is to say, he's younger than he has previously claimed to be.

Let me take you back to 1936. In that year the whole village sighed with relief when Sid's parents, Henry Kipper and Dot Spratt, married each other, because it meant that nobody else would have to marry either of them. They set up home on the edge of the village in Box Cottage and seemed quite happy, in a miserable sort of way.

Henry and Dot never wanted children, but at the outbreak of the Second World War they saw the advantage of the extra rations that a child would bring. So they registered the birth of a son, Sid, who at that stage didn't actually exist. This arrangement worked very well until the end of the war. When the lax wartime bureaucracy was tightened up it became clear that they might be required to produce the boy. No longer could they claim, as they had, that he had been 'ejaculated to London'. So Henry enquired of the vicar how they might go about having a child and, after some incredulity, they went ahead. Dot finally, if reluctantly, gave birth to the real, flesh-and-blood Sid on 21 September 1946. But it's not easy being an unwanted child, as Sid recalls:

> I sort of got the feeling that I weren't wanted when the rationing got eased. What give me that feeling was when mother used to leave me in shops or on buses, or anywhere in fact. I once spent three days in a cake shop in North Walsham before they managed to trace her and make her take me back. Of course, that was nothing personal. Eventually I learned to keep an eye out for her trying to sneak off. I reckon that must be where I picked up the habit of following women home.

By all accounts Sid was a happy little boy, although something of a loner. He spent much of his time practising putting his finger in his ear and singing folk songs. He loved nature and when he was not needed to work around the house he would go for long walks. He knew where every pheasant and rabbit lived, and he sang to them.

From an early age Sid was expected to work for his keep.

It has to be said that Sid and education never saw eye to eye. The biggest problem was Sid's singing. It was in his blood and he had no wish to do anything else. At the age of five, however, he was dragged kicking and screaming to start his formal education at Trunch Bored School. It was a day he will never forget.

I weren't kicking and screaming – I was dancing and singing. But I do remember we had a bit of trouble over the singing. Miss Eels, the teacher, spent all her time telling me not to sing in the classroom. Well, not all her time, obviously. I mean, for a start, she used to go home of an evening. Mind you, I never went home with her, so I don't know for sure she din't spend her time there telling me not to sing in the classroom. But there was one time she din't tell me not to sing and that was during singing lessons. She threw me out for them. She said I put the others off.

Eventually a compromise was reached whereby Sid could sing whenever he liked, but had to leave the classroom and do it in the boys toilets which were situated at the far end of the playground. In fact he spent so much time there that he taught himself to read from the graffiti on the walls. However, Sid was not a complete failure at primary school. In fact he gained a qualification of which he is very proud.

I got a certificate for 'Fifty Yards Breast-stroke Theory' – the school din't have no swimming pool, so we couldn't do the practical. I was very good at the breast-stroking, though I never could get the hang of crawling – Cyril Cockle got a distinction for that.

On leaving primary school Sid earned a place at Borstal, but his ambition was thwarted, as his parents couldn't afford the uniform. So he went, with the rest of his class-mates, to the nearby Knapton Academy where he was not allowed to sing in class. Nor was he allowed to leave the class to sing because the boys toilets were situated next to the headmaster's office and the walls were thin. So Sid took to truancy. But, in a small village, where everyone knows everyone's business, he quickly had to become an expert at evading the Attendance Officer. He spent a lot of time lurking in the woods – a habit he retains to this day.

I never bothered none about doing well at school. Even then all I wanted to do was sing and play the accompaniments, so I couldn't see no point in getting no big qualifications. My Uncle Walter was teaching me the piano by the traditional method of beating time on my fingers with the lid, apart from which I taught myself the other instruments. Now that weren't easy, 'cos of course I din't know how to play them in order to teach myself. It was like the deaf telling the deaf, really. But most of all I was practising the unaccompanied singing. Well, it's not easy to evade the Tendency Officer if you're dragging a piano, is it?

Sid, with his older cousin Len, selling pigeons in North Walsham in 1958.
The thumb print is thought to be George Kipper's.

4

The Golden Buoy

When Sid left school in 1960 he was apprenticed to his uncle, George Kipper. The exact nature of George's business is not clear, but it seems to have involved such traditional crafts as 'dealing', 'flogging' and 'following lorries waiting for things to drop off the back'.

> I come under the influence with Uncle George, when he was back in the village after a spell away, pleasing Her Majesty. He's a lovely singer is George – much better than my old father. It's a shame he has to help the police so much with their enquiries or he could be famous without the 'in'. George taught me all I knew at the time. Mind you, that weren't a lot. I mean, George knew a lot, but he always used to say 'If I told you all I knew then you'd know as much as I do, plus anything you might have picked up for yourself, and then I'd have to be your apprentice, so you'll just have to find things out the hard way like I did, young fellow-me-lad.' He always used to say that. Unless you offered to buy him a drink, of course, and then he said 'A pint of the usual.'

But, as much of George's business seemed to revolve around pubs, and in particular the Old Goat Inn in Trunch, Sid had lots of opportunities to hear his uncle sing, and with his keen ear he rapidly learned all that George knew. As an apprentice he was not allowed to sing in the pub himself – singing was considered to be man's work and until a Truncheon had gone through the strange ritual which took place on his twenty-first birthday he was expected to keep quiet, and buy the beer.

> Kid's nowadays have it soft. At that time of the day they used to say 'One boy is worth half a man, two boys is worth half a boy and three boys aren't worth nothing at all.' But they couldn't stop me singing in the privy of my own house, although they wished they could when they wanted to go in there for a sing themselves.

In 1964, at the age of eighteen, Sid began his National Service. This was a very difficult thing for him to do, not least because National Service had been abolished some years earlier. But Sid has never been one to shun a problem and he managed to get the Mundesley Dark Infantry to take him on for a year.

> I got fed up with people going on about how the army made them what they were. I mean, looking at some of them, you'd think they ought to go and ask for their money back. Howsomever, I thought I'd like to give it a go. I thought wrong as a matter of fact, because I hated every minute of it. Well, I tell a lie – I didn't hate *every* minute. I hated every minute except for about twenty minutes in September, with the Colonel's daughter. I quite enjoyed those minutes.

Actually, Sid and the army got on surprisingly well. He has always been a smart dresser, so the uniform was no trouble to him.

> I was always one for dressing smart and up to the minute. I mean, I was the first person in Trunch to wear drainpipe trousers – that would have been in about 1964, as far as I recall. Then again, they all laughed when I moved on to flares in 1978. I'm a bit of a trend settler, as a matter of fact. Of course that's where a lot of these modern folk-singers get it wrong. You see, I was brought up to dress in my best for the singing – it's a mark of respect. But these new people, a lot of them don't even wear a tie. It's all Arran sweaters, which are only correct for singing Scottish songs. It's a shame, 'cos some of them aren't bad singers. It's just the clothes that let them down.

He was also very good at soldierly activities like creeping about at night with a gun and shooting things. Square bashing took him some time to come to terms with, but once he had worked out that it was really just a flat-footed sort of morris dance he quickly got the hang of it. Consequently he marched with bells on his ankles, and, since no one could find a regulation that actually banned it, and the years of training under his Uncle George had made him an excellent barrack-room lawyer, they couldn't stop him.

Sid Kipper, dressed to trill.

Every now and again I got leave, so I kept in touch with what was going on in the village. There was a new vicar, who we've still got, except, of course, he's an old vicar now. That was Rev. 'Call-me-Derek' Bream. We didn't get on too well at first. He was having Hops in the village hall and that sort of thing. I never went – I was too busy having hops in the Old Goat Inn. But over the years he's made quite a difference to our village. Well, either that or it's got different of its own accord and he just happened to be there.

Derek (known to some as Dingley Del) has been an important influence on Sid's career. His songwriting, in particular, brought other sorts of music to Sid's attention and, over the years, Sid has sung a few of Derek's songs himself.

Well, sometimes I get bored with the old songs, and fancy something a bit more groovy and up to date. More often, though, it's the audience who get bored and need waking up. That's when I give them one of Del's numbers. By the end of one of them they're begging me to go back to the old songs again.

Derek Bream as 'Lust', in Snow White and the Seven Deadly Sins.

A Plaice in the Sun

After National Service Sid went back to work for his Uncle George, and in 1967 came the great moment when he went through the rite of passage into manhood and public singing. The ceremony itself is a closely guarded secret, known only to the adult males of St Just-near-Trunch and I've been unable to get any of them to describe it to me. Certainly, it involves a lot more than Sid claims.

> Well, it's just a sort of passing-out ceremony, really. You have a few drinks, sing a song, have a few more drinks, sing some more songs, and so on, until you eventually pass out. Actually I hold the record for the person who had the most drinks and sang the most songs before passing out. Well, I do if you only count the people who lived to tell the tale.

Once Sid was allowed to sing in public people had to admit what, in fact, they already knew – that here was the sort of singer that comes along only once in a generation, if that. And what's more, he was a genuine all-rounder. From front-bar chorus to back-room ballad, Sid had real class – and that's not to mention snug-bar story-telling and courtyard dancing. The lad was so talented, so superior to the older singers, so much better than any of his contemporaries, that in no time at all they were heartily fed up with him.

> Well, I mean, that was just jealousy, weren't it? I was better than them, louder than them, I knew more songs than them and they din't like it. It din't bother me none, though, because by then I

7

was being asked to go along to other pubs in the area to sing there. I used to get free beer and the like. You see, people today don't realise what it was like then. If you were one of the top singers then you were somebody. I'm not sure just who you were, but you were somebody. And that somebody was somebody who was respected and looked up at. All the young women wanted to be seen in your company. Mind you, that weren't so wonderful, 'cos as soon as you got them alone, and there was nobody to see them with you, they din't want to know you not any more.

At about this time Sid had a brush with fame. It happened one night when he was singing in the White Hearse Inn, in North Walsham, when a stranger in a suit came in and sat by the bar. This meant, of course, that he was sitting near Sid, as singers always sat by the bar so as to avoid any interruption in the flow of free pints. He was visibly impressed by the power and range of Sid's voice.

He was – he was visibly impressed. You could see that. So when I had a break from the singing this bloke in the suit started me up in conversation and asked a lot of questions. He said did I want to be a pop star, like that Cilla Black? He said did I realise there was a gap in the market? Well, I knew the answer to that, so I said yes I did – that was where the gents' lavatory used to stand before it blew down. He said no, not North Walsham market – the record market. He said someone called Bob Dylan had been electrocuted, so they was looking for a new folk star and did I want to be 'it'? Well, I said I couldn't be 'it' because I had both feet off the ground when he touched me, so it din't count, but after a bit I realised he wanted me to make hit records and the like. So then I had some questions for him. The first one was whose round was it? He said we weren't in a round. So I asked did he realise that if he bought me a pint I'd be in his debt and he took the hint, and bought me a pint. Well, by the end of the night I was in his debt a lot, but that was alright 'cos I din't have no intention of paying him back. You see, there was a fly in his ointment – I couldn't do my own songs. He said old traditional songs din't make no money for nobody, so they wouldn't do. Well, that was what I was known for, so I said no thank you and thought no more about it. Not till I heard he'd gone on to Sheringham and signed up some bloke called the Singing Postman. Then I realised I'd missed an opportunity, and you know what they say – opportunity never knocks twice in the same place.

The Silence of the Clams

Seeing the Singing Postman rise to international fame and riches, such that he had his postman's uniforms handmade at Burtons the Tailor, Sid might easily have become bitter. So he did.

I thought that should have been me on 'On Your Marks, Get Set, Go', having all them roadies dancing round in their short skirts. I didn't want to sing just to a few people in the pub no more. I thought I should be doing big places, like Cromer Pier, like he was doing. It took a long time to get over that. In fact I don't reckon I really got over it till that Ralph Harris recorded one of his songs – then I realised what an awful mistake it would have been.

George Kipper being off the scene at the time, being 'unavoidably detained' yet again, Sid concentrated on his own business of supplying game – although some customers found his habit of delivering the goods in the early hours of the morning somewhat disconcerting.

I still used to sing to myself, but I only used to do it at night, in the woods. Mind you, the gamekeeper used to find that hard to believe when he wanted to know what I was doing there.

These were Sid's wilderness years, at least as far as public performance went. Not that he lacked offers.

The Womens' Bright Hour was forever after me to perform for them, but I thought that would be a bit of a comedown after having nearly been famous, so I refused. My cousin Annie used to be after me to sing too. She said I owed it to my roots to carry on the old traditions and wouldn't it be a shame if the old songs died out, and all that squit. But I din't take no notice because everyone knew she hadn't been right in the head since she went to North Walsham Grammar School for Girls. I don't mean she actually got taught there, but she did once visit it as third reserve for the netball team, and, like I say, she was never the same after.

And so, for some fifteen years, the finest voice of a generation lay dormant. When the singing started in the Old Goat Inn Sid would simply order another pint and sip it with a brooding look in his eye. Even the most lusty chorus song could not tempt him to join in. He didn't step-dance or tell stories or perform, or participate in any way shape or form whatsoever.

Which is just a fancy way of saying I din't do nothing, which is exactly what I did do. Mind you, I done other things. I done my crafts, like making sweetcorn dollies, and so on, and I done my game business, and I played my cricket and my bowls, and so on. And in my spare time I was seeing a bit of Raquel Whelk – well, I saw several bits of her, actually, but never all in the same place. She was always playing hard to get was Raquel, but she weren't a very good player, so she always lost. If you don't believe me, ask anyone.

Sid is often asked, especially by Raquel, why he has never married. After all, at this stage of his life Sid was all set to settle down in a small village, where a wife would be an asset if only to stop the tongues of the old women from wagging.

Ah, but I had a better way of stopping them wagging. I used to go up to one of the old women and tell him straight that my business was none of his business, and that went for my personal life too. That and a good stare used to do the trick. And if you want to know why I never got married I'll tell you the same thing.

And so the years went by with Sid singing only in private for his own amusement.

A rare picture of the camera-shy Raquel Whelk,
following her triumph in the Miss Rule competition, 1969.

Return of the Octupi

But of course Sid did start singing in public again, for, in 1980, a rumour began to circulate that the Cockle family were better singers than the Kippers. Sid's father, Henry Kipper, decided that he'd better start singing in public himself, in order to protect the family name from the gossips. Sid soon realised that he would have to join him, in order to protect the family name from his father.

> Well, he'd only have proved the rumour right, wouldn't he? I mean, if George had been about I wouldn't have bothered, 'cos even George could sing the Cockle family into a cocked snook. But with his being away again there was only me to save father from himself.

Henry Kipper was a proud man. This was always a surprise to those who met him, since it was immediately apparent there was little of which he could be proud. Nevertheless he had become custodian of the family tradition when his own father, Billy Kipper, died in 1948, leaving his elder son the blue family songbook.

> Mind you that weren't so much, 'cos Uncle George got the red family songbook. Years ago Billy used to get up in the Old Goat and say 'Would you like one out of the red book or the blue book', and they always asked for the red book, 'cos that was the one with the good songs in. But my father always pretended the red book never existed, which was silly really 'cos it was there all the time, large as life, propping up the wonky leg on George's wardrobe.

Sid was later to resurrect the songs from the red book when he went solo in 1992 – but I'm getting ahead of the story.

> Well, I'm not. What happened was father started to go round singing Billy's old songs and I thought that was my duty to go along, and help him out. I used to do what they call 'counter-melody'. The idea was to try and counter what father was doing to the melody by distracting people with some different notes. After a while I got him sounding quite good. Later, we decided we ought to have some sort of a stage name (although we never sang on no stages, so it was more of a corner-of-the-pub name really). We thought of loads, but none of them was quite right. We tried The Sugarbeatles and The Bloody Moos, and things like that, but father wasn't happy with none of them. He said we had to have a name what went along with the serious old folk-songs we was doing. It was Aunt Ruby who eventually come up with one.

So began the career of Sid Kipper and Henry Kipper, soon known throughout north-east Norfolk by their snappy new name, the Kipper Family. Henry, a born-again defender of the folk tradition, insisted that they only perform the songs which his own father had painstakingly written in what was now a dog-eared, blue, foolscap notebook. Not only the songs, but also the manner of singing them was to be preserved just as Billy had handed them on.

> They had this thing they called the oral tradition round our way. Very popular it was. The idea was the fathers used to pass on all their old songs to the sons – where they could be traced. That was the idea, but most people's fathers was only human, if that, so they kept a couple of the best songs back for themselves and passed on the rest. That happened for generation after generation, until you get to where we are today – with all the old rubbish left.

A fight once broke out in the Nelson's Arm in Knapton when Cyril Cockle declared that Billy had only written the songs down as examples of what nobody liked any more and proceeded to silence the pair by putting ten pence into the jukebox to play *Stand By Your Man*.

Yes, well, we were doing all these old songs about jolly ploughboys and their jolly ploughs, and that was all we was allowed. Well, no, to be fair, father did let me do one of George's now and again, but that was only because he was family and father felt sorry for him, what with him not being able to get out, and do them for himself.

So, for more than a year father and son toured the area, singing their old songs to people who didn't want to hear them, each too proud, stubborn, and stupid to be the first one to suggest giving it up.

Father and son keeping up the tradition.

There but for the Grace of Cod

And this is where I enter the story. One day in 1982, my friend Dick Nudds and I received a letter from Sid's cousin, Annie Kipper, telling us about a traditional singing family from Trunch. Dick insisted this was a practical joke and the place couldn't exist. But I knew better. I had distant cousins in Trunch and my aunt once passed through the village when lost. So, being enthusiasts for traditional song, Dick and I went in search of Henry and Sid.

11

I can sort of remember sitting in the Old Goat one afternoon, just innocently drinking after hours, when these two blokes with beards come in. The whole pub went quiet, just like in the Westerns – except there weren't no piano player. Well, no, actually there was a piano player, but you wouldn't have known that 'cos there weren't no piano. Ernie Spratt, the landlord, he asked what did they want? They said they was sorry to come in when the pub was closed but they was looking for the Kipper Family. Ernie said never mind that, what did they want to drink? So they ordered a couple of pints of Old Nasty, which was their first big mistake, other than coming in the pub to start with. After a bit they asked about the Kipper Family again, so Ernie asked what they wanted us for. They said they'd heard how we knew some old songs what we might not want. Well, that was how we knew something was up. You see, that was exactly what Cecil Sharphouse had said to my Great Uncle Albert sixty years before. So Ernie asked the six-and-four-penny question – had they got any money? Yes, they said, so he sold them a couple more pints of Old Nasty. They looked as if they thought they was getting nowhere, but they weren't – they was getting drunk.

We only drank three pints as far as I remember. But I will never forget the odd couple at the table in the corner of the bar who were watching us in a disconcerting manner. There was an old man with a white beard and a younger man with a scar on his cheek. And then they started to sing – loud enough at first, and then slowly fading as we slid, unconscious, from our bar stools.

Star Fish

As soon as we were discharged from Cromer Hospital we went back to the village, and, to cut a long story short, persuaded Sid and Henry to place their careers in our hands. For a year or more we polished these rough diamonds until we thought they were ready for the big wide world. But was the big wide world ready for them? It was. Their rise to fame was meteoric. In 1984 they turned professional and were voted 'Most Promising Newcomers' by the readers of *Folk Roots*, the most prestigious folk magazine in the country. Henry was particularly flattered at being described as a newcomer in his seventieth year. Thus began seven years of touring, recording, and radio and TV work.

It was like a fairy story, really, with me and father as the fairies.

They were heaped with awards and certificates, perhaps the most glamorous being Radio Orwell's award as 'Most Popular Club Act' in 1985.

That was a mistake, of course, 'cos we din't use no clubs in our act at all. I think they must have got us mixed up with some jugglers who were going about at the time. They was called the Skipper Family. They used to do a lot of work on Radio Norfolk at one time, although after a while the novelty of a juggling act on the wireless wore off. One of them, Keith Skipper, still did it till recently, but he had to interview people and play records during the juggling to make it sound a bit more interesting. In the end they got fed up with the holes in the ceiling and got rid of him. I believe he does his juggling in the paper now.

Suddenly these two Norfolk 'boys' were touring from the Shetlands to Cornwall – which wasn't one of the best-arranged tours, since they had no engagements in between. The Kipper Family were soon established as firm favourites on the folk scene. Their first album, 'Since Time Immoral', was followed by five others, the last being an edited recording of Henry's retirement party, 'In The Family Way'. Sid and Henry also appeared with their own band, The New Trunch Coronation Band, and toured several times with the Rev. Derek Bream.

Left to right: Tim Laycock, Pennie Harris, Ursula Pank and Tony Hall.

It seemed they could go on for ever. But seven years of touring and singing, and sleeping in strange beds took it's toll on the old man – and on the younger man too.

> I din't have no trouble with the touring and the singing, and the sleeping in the strange beds – the only trouble I had was having to tour and sing, and sleep in strange beds with the old man. He snores, you know – and not just when he's asleep. But the main thing was he was holding me back. I mean, that was kept a secret at the time, but I was asked to join the Fairport Convention, but they din't want father, so I had to turn it down. Also, I wanted to play a lot more musical instruments, but father wouldn't have it. He said 'You'll play all them instruments over my dead body,' so I said 'Yes, I would, and the sooner the better.'

To those of us 'in the know' relations between father and son were clearly becoming strained. It was the little things, like one of them leaving the room whenever the other came in. I knew matters were getting serious when Henry failed to accept Sid's offer of a drink one night.

> Things got worse between us when the *Trunch Trumpet* voted me 'Best Young Thruster of 1991'. Father was livered. He wanted to know why, if he could be a 'Most Promising Newcomer' in 1984, he couldn't be a 'Young Thruster' in 1991? I said he should be glad he couldn't enter 'cos he'd be sure to come last. He said he'd forgotten more about folk-singing with one hand tied behind his back than he'd ever known and I should hold my row. I said I was surprised 'cos I thought he'd forgotten more than that. There was a whole lot more like that, but the upshoot was we sent each other to Coventry for a month. Mind you, we still sang together, which was a bit difficult, 'cos we couldn't discuss what we was going to sing. So it was a question of being first off the mark, singing what you wanted, and the other one had to catch up.

The strain begins to show.

Things got worse and worse with me and father, and in the end there was only one solution. We organised a surprise retirement party for him, and the whole thing was a café complète, whatever that is. Well, whatever it is, the whole thing was one of them. We done a farewell tour, and with one bound I was free.

Shortly before Henry's enforced retirement, the English Folk-song and Dance Society had announced the founding of an Old Folkies Home, and asked for anyone who knew of any worn-out old folkies to get in touch. They were inundated with replies, but Henry got a place on the grounds of seniority (a number of the worn-out folkies nominated were only in their early forties). The home was a model establishment, with regular activities for the inmates. For instance, every day there was a 'singaround' in the lounge, where the old people could sing long boring ballads to each other with their hearing-aids turned off. Once a week, as a treat, a folk-song collector would come in with a microphone and pretend to record them.

But now we have lost the old man. Not that he's dead – not as far as we know. He simply broke out and went on the run, and no one has ever bothered to look for him. At the time of writing there are rumours that he has become an old-age traveller, roaming the country with a psychedelic zimmer frame.

As long as he's doing what he wants, then fair enough – good luck to him. I just hope he's miserable.

Going Sole-oh

And so, on the second Friday of 1992, Sid gathered up his music stand and instruments, along with some songs from his Uncle George's red songbook, and set off for his first solo performance, in Chichester.

> Of course, that was a bit nerve wrecking, but inside I was loudly confident. After all, I only had to play my instruments and sing my songs. I knew I could do both them things alright. The only thing I hadn't actually practised was doing them both at the same time. But I needn't have worried. I got to this folk club, which is upstairs at a pub, and they were busy putting out the chairs. But after I'd explained that I weren't a dance band they put all the chairs back in again and we waited for people to arrive.

Gradually the room filled up and only a few people said 'I thought Sid was the old one – that's who I came to see.' And all too soon Sid was on his feet introducing his first song.

> I launched off into 'The Stick Of Rhubarb' and right from the start they was with me. What's more, they was still with me at the end, which is always a good sign 'cos sometimes they sneak off if you sing with your eyes closed and you don't notice till there's no applause. All in all that was a great start to my career as a solo megostar.

Since then Sid has been supported by a fully professional set-up, with myself as his manager, a record deal and agents who really know 'the business'. No longer is Sid dependant on Ernie Spratt taking phone calls at the Old Goat Inn and writing his engagements down on cigarette packets. Success has followed success and now Sid is appearing everywhere, live, on radio, and in print. It all seems to be working very well for the man from Trunch.

> I've never been busier – I'm working all the time now. Mind you, my uncle George would spin in his grave if he was dead. He always reckon that anyone who really wants to work should jolly well get on their bike and go for a long ride until the feeling wears off, and then go down the pub and forget all about it.

And the rest, as they say, is history.

> They're bloody right, as well. I can't remember when I last had a rest.

Sid resting.

VERSE TWO – THE MUSIC

In which he sings of love and war, sea and land,
wondrous creatures, and crabs.

Here we have the heart of this book – a collection of some of the gems of the finest folk-song tradition in the country. Most of these songs have been handed down through the generations, as described by Sid elsewhere. But the Trunch tradition is not a static one. New songs are being added all the time, just as old ones are being forgotten. This book also contains songs from Sid's repertoire by three living writers.

GEORGE KIPPER is probably the most important of the three. For some years now the Trunch One has penned song after song which has just failed to succeed. For instance, he had high hopes of a song entitled 'I'd Like to Teach the World to Sin', but those hopes were dashed by the appearance of another, strangely similar, song. Much the same happened with 'The Streets of Loddon' and a wonderful song about being lost in the dark at sea called 'Have You Got a Light Buoy?' Perhaps when the police no longer need his help with their enquiries he will be able to change his luck.

DEREK BREAM writes songs about issues. Be it his faith, his personal relationships or his support for the green movement, his hallmark is passion. He has written songs for Sting, Tina Turner and Victoria de los Angelis, to name but a few. It's a crying shame that none of them has ever sung any of them. But their loss is Sid's gain, as Sid therefore has his pick of Derek's songs.

KEVIN KIPPER is still an apprentice to the song-writing trade. Nevertheless he shows signs of following in his grandfather George's footsteps, in more ways than one, so perhaps we should make the most of him while he is still freely available. His song 'The Christmas Collapso' found its way on to a Kipper Family album and his contribution here is his collaboration with Derek Bream on 'Jam Tomorrow'.

I would like to thank all three personally for allowing their songs to be included in this book, but since I haven't actually asked their permission that would perhaps be inappropriate.

How To Do Folk-singing
by Sid Kipper

Folk-singing is not so easy as it looks. Top-class folk-singing like what I do needs you to learn things like growing a beard, putting your finger in your ear without using a mirror and where to buy waistcoats. But that's all too hard for you what are just starting. What you want now are a few tips, so here's some to get you going.

Now it help with folk-singing if you don't know nothing about music. You see, people what know about music get all mixed up with things like quays and bars and crotches, and the like. But in folk-singing you just have the words and the tune, and you use the one to sing the other. Some people use the tune to sing the words and some people use the words to sing the tune – that's all a matter of taste. And if you've got any taste you'll do what I do, and use the tune to sing the words. So your first job with the songs in this book is to learn the tunes, and then forget about all the lines and dots, and stuff like that. You'll have to do that, anyhow, because the tunes in the book are just the tunes of the first verses. In folk-singing you have to bend the tune of each verse to make it fit the words, otherwise you end up with some words or notes left over. Some people can't do that, so they play the guitar to cover up the gaps.

So, you've learned the tunes and you're ready to learn how to sing the songs. But, before that, you have to decide how you're going to block up your nose to get the proper folk-singing sound. Now, for a long time people thought this was just a fashion, brung over to Norfolk by the Flems. But they've done this research and they reckon if you have a blocked up nose then you get a sort of echo effect round the back of the skull. At one time of the day people used to get this by singing with their fingers up their noses, but that was all stopped by the Victorians, who din't like that sort of thing. So then people had to put their fingers in their ears instead. Nowadays a lot of the top singers have their noses blocked up by surgery. Some of them have also had their brains removed, to increase the echo. But, for beginners like what you are, I reckon a couple of bits of cotton wool will do for now.

Okay, so you've learned the tunes, you've got a couple of bits of cotton wool up your nose and the next thing is to get a note. Any old note will do, just so long as it's not too high or too low. Of course, you won't know if it's too high or too low until you sing the song, so don't worry about it. In fact, I wish I'd never mentioned it. This is the note you start on. It could be the note you finish on, too, but it don't matter if you don't, 'cos by the time you get there everyone will have forgotten what note you started on anyway – that's known as the 'Sliding Scale' and is specially important for mining songs.

Right, now you've learned the tunes, got a couple of bits of cotton wool stuck up your nose and you've got a note. The next thing to do is posture. That's why folk-singers do it standing up. The easiest way is to practice singing with a book on your head. The best book would be this one, 'cos that way if you forget the words you can take it off and look them up.

Well, now you've leaned the tunes, got a couple of bits of cotton wool stuck up your nose and you've got a book on your head. But have you still got your note? If not, get another one – there's plenty more where that came from. Because now the big moment have arrived. Now you know more about folk-singing than most people, so you're ready to sing the songs.

Allan Barber

You vir-gins all I pray draw near, 'tis you I am in-vit-ing, I'll sing a song of sick-ness, pain and death, and ter-rib-le hand-writ-ing.

This is the first song in the book, due to it being in pathetic order. Of course, you don't have to sing the songs in pathetic order – you can sing them in any order you like. Or even one you don't like, if you like. You can sing them in total disorder if you prefer.

This first song is what they call a 'broadside ballad'. So it's not as old as it might be. You see, the oldest ballads was what was called 'narrowside ballads'. They were written on long, narrow bits of paper, but they were a bugger to write, 'cos you had to have a rhyme at the end of every line, which was every two or three words. So ballad writing din't really catch on until someone invented the idea of turning the bit of paper sideways and so come up with the 'broadside ballad'. These was a lot easier to write, because they din't have hardly no rhymes at all. And even then they din't have to rhyme very much, 'cos by the time you got to the rhyme everyone had forgotten what it was supposed to rhyme with in the first place.

This song is actually about Cromer Pier, which was made famous a while back when it got hit by a boat. I told them years ago: I said 'If you leave that thing sticking out to sea you're bound to get boats run into it', but they never took no notice. But the song isn't just about Cromer Pier, 'cos that wouldn't be a very long song. Although, actually, there is a song just about Cromer Pier, which only goes to prove my point. It used to be sung by my famous music hall uncle, Jimmy 'Am I Boring You' Kipper and it goes:

It's long and it's straight, and it sticks out to sea;
Diddle de diddle de diddle de dee.

That's all there is to it. Mind you, it was ideal for singing at the Trunch Empire, 'cos nobody stayed on stage for long there anyhow, due to it being so rough. They used to reckon they left 'no turn unstoned' at the Trunch Empire.

This song is a good one to start the book with because it shows the sort of trouble you can get into when you're folk-singing. You see, this song do cause a bit of confusion at times and people don't know what to do when you sing the first line. Now I should have thought that was clear enough – you're either a virgin or you aren't, aren't you? I mean, I suppose you could have been so drunk you weren't sure either way, but even then you could ask someone – always supposing you could remember who to ask, of course. Anyhow, what I do when I sing the song is ask everyone to ignore the first line. Otherwise a whole load of people might get up and rush towards you, then they'd be embarrassed. On the other hand, nobody might get up and that could be embarrassing too.

So, all in all, it might be best not to sing this song at all and get on to the next one.

You virgins all I pray draw near, 'tis you I am inviting,
I'll sing a song of sickness, pain and death, and terrible handwriting.

It's of a lad of Cromer town, who dwelt down by the harbour;
He was a pale and a sickly youth, and they called him Allan Barber.

This young man had a tender heart, likewise a full-sore liver;
He always feared infection and he often had the shivers.

Now Allan loved a maiden fair, stout hearted and courageous,
But he shunned her when she grew thick around the waist,
In case it was contagious.

One May Day down at Cromer pier, the lads and lasses busy,
A-dancing round the maypole, but it made poor Allan dizzy.

'Oh doctor, doctor, I feel ill – please write my love a letter,
To tell her she's the only one can make me feel ... better.'

So the doctor's writ a letter long to Allan's heart's desire,
But she could not read the writing so she tossed it on the fire.

Oh curséd be that cruel note, it burned like flaming tinder;
The house took fire and she was burned unto a flaming cinder.

When Allan heard his love was dead he had a strange reaction;
He clean forgot his illness, for he loved her to distraction.

So Allan took his love to church, not to be consummated,
But to bury her in the cold, cold clay – though she'd already been cremated.

And he stood by her open grave, his tears a flowing river;
He cried 'Bury me beside my love' – so they pushed him in with her.

Oh bitter, bitter was his fall, his landing still more bitter:
For Allan died the very hour when he had ne'er felt fitter.

So you virgins all this warning take: if life you'd be enhancing,
Put not your faith in doctors' arts and never try morris dancing.

All Things Are Quite Equal

A young person was a-walking one morning in May;
Met a second young person a-walking that way.
Said the first of these people: 'I have Spanish leather,
And oh, 'tis my wish we were bonded together.'

Chorus
All things being equal our screws will be loose;
What's sauce for the gander is juice for the goose.

'For the way I respond to the charms that thou haste
I just cannot tell you, lest you feel harassed.
But you are so comely and so fair of face,
How I long to enter your personal space.'

Said the other 'I'm willing, if you would agree,
To place you above me and then underneath.'
To a mossy green bank these two persons did haste,
And there, in a meaningful way, interfaced.

Both parties were eager, both parties were brisk;
Both failed to ensure 'gainst a third-party risk.
And so, nine months later, as I understand,
A third person singular came, all unplanned.

Now the first person declared without guile;
'For your sweet sake I would lay down my life-style.'
So these two were married, like sister and brother,
And over the threshold they carried each other.

22

This song is all to do with what they call 'Partial Correctness'. You see, these days people get upset far too easy. I mean, when I was a boy we used to spend a whole evening trying to get someone upset and when they finally did, well, you felt you'd achieved something. But nowadays they get upset before you can drop your hat, so there's no fun in it at all.

The people at the English Folk-song and Dance Society, who are in charge of folk-singing, realised that a lot of the things people get upset about come in a lot of the folk-songs. I mean, people get upset about hunting and there's a lot of hunting in folk-songs. And whaling – a lot of people get upset about that. And murdering people and cutting them up into little bits – that's another one. In fact, whatever you get up and sing, you can bet your bottom that someone will get aerated about it. It's not like the old days. I mean, we used to have a saying 'Sticks and stones may break my bones, but an old folk-song will never harm me', but that all seem to have gone bye the bye.

So the idea was to get some new old folk-songs what wouldn't upset nobody, so they took some of the old songs and redone them. There was things like 'People When Young Never Co-habit with a Senior Citizen' and 'Oh No, John, No (And When I Say No I Mean No)'. And, of course, this one what's printed here. The whole thing never really caught on though, because people din't know if they was men's songs or women's songs, so nobody sang them in case they were singing the wrong sort. Take this song, for instants. Originally this was an old song about boy meets girl – there were no persons in it at all. They met, they done what boys and girls do, and then they got married. Everyone knew where they were in them days, like it or not. You either got married or you lived in sin. But now there's no living in sin, so that takes all the fun out of it and you might as well just get married, and be done with it. Well, if that's Partial Correctness you can leave me out.

Sid receives an award for 'Partial Correctness'.

23

The Black Bonny Hare

Fellatio

On the fif-teenth of May, at the break of the day, With me hare washed and brushed to the woods I did stray; I - I sure-ly was game, and if the sports-man proved fair, I - I hoped that he'd fire at my black bon-ny hare.

On the fifteenth of May, at the break of the day,
With me hare washed and brushed, to the woods I did stray;
I surely was game, and if the sportsman proved fair,
I hoped that he'd fire at my black bonny hare.

I met this young man with a breech-loader there;
Says he 'I am seeking the black bonny hare.
But first, how d-you do? Weather's nice; looks like snow.'
Says I 'Me young sportsman, why ramble you so?'

The answer he gave me, his answer was 'Oh,
They say the black bonny hare must be stalked nice and slow';
Says I 'Not so slow, for I declare and I vow
My hare's up and running, you must take your aim now.'

Oh I laid myself down with my face to the skies,
I said 'Pull out your ramrod and your bullets likewise;
Take the firing position, but don't shoot till you ought,
For the longer the chase, love, the better the sport.'

Oh a bird in the bush is worth two in the hand,
But a shot in the dark is more the way of a man.
I felt his heart quiver, and I knew what he'd done;
Says he 'Have you had enough of me old sporting gun?'

The answer I gave him, my answer was 'Nay –
It's too often young sportsmen like you come this way!
You flush the hare up, but don't play the game fair;
You bang, but don't finish the black bonny hare.'

'Now your ramrod is limber, your bullets all fired;
The hare it lies gasping, but has not yet expired.
If you are a sportsman then you'll do what you can,
And you'll finish the black bonny hare off by hand.'

Bobby Dazzler

Romeo

Bob-by Daz-zler's gone to seed, legs all buc-kled at the knee, When he gets home he'll fall a-sleep, shod-dy Bob-by Daz-zler. Once his eyes were bright-ly blue, of a clear and shi-ning hue, Now they're dull and blood-shot too, grog-gy Bob-by Daz-zler.

Chorus
Bobby Dazzler's gone to seed,
Legs all buckled at the knee,
When he gets home he'll fall asleep,
Shoddy Bobby Dazzler.

Once his eyes were brightly blue,
Of a clear and shining hue,
Now they're dull and bloodshot too,
Groggy Bobby Dazzler.

Once the girls he did bedazzle,
Every night out on the razzle,
Now he lives with Reg and Basil
In a home for clapped-out sailors.

Once he strode around so grand,
All the girls fought for his hand,
Now he's just a dirty old man,
Sorry Bobby Dazzler.

Once, no matter what he drank,
His mind was sharp for any prank;
Now he's two bricks short of a plank,
Dotty Bobby Dazzler.

Once he was a proper gent,
Like a flashing blade he went,
Now he's a blunt instrument,
Ploddy Bobby Dazzler.

Once his back was ramrod straight,
Now he's bent and overweight;
Pretty soon he'll be the late
Bonny Bobby Dazzler.

Now the news has come today,
Bobby Dazzler's passed away;
All the girls will shout 'Hurray!
Goodbye Bobby Dazzler,
Goodbye Bobby Dazzler.'

Bobby Dazzler came from Bacton. He was born there, he lived there and he died there. So really he din't so much come from Bacton as stay put in Bacton, as a matter of fact. He was famous around our parts for running away from sea. He only went out the once, and when they come back he said he weren't never going no more, on account of the boat going up and down. He said it was daft having the boat go up and down like that – it'd make more sense to keep the boat still, and let the sea go up and down instead. So he left the Dazzler family fishing business and set himself up as a mole catcher. He weren't much good at mole catching, though. Well, no, he was very good at mole catching, but terrible at mole killing. He hadn't the heart for it, so he used to catch all these moles and then let them go again. Eventually he teamed up with my great, great, great uncle, 'Dirty' Herbert Kipper, who couldn't catch a mole to save his life, but really liked killing them. Bobby lived to a ripe old age, due to never having a wash.

The Bodyline Collapso

Subuteo

Cric - ket, it was -n't cric - ket, at Trunch where I saw it;

Cric - ket, it was - n't cric - ket, at Trunch where I saw it; When

Trunch came in to bat, the bowl -ers tried to knock them flat;

Burn - ing -ham said it was -n't fair, 'cos they got the runs off their un - der -wear.

With those two great pals of mine, Al - bert Kip -per and Doug -las Sar -dyne.

Cricket, it wasn't cricket, at Trunch where I saw it;
Cricket, it wasn't cricket, at Trunch where I saw it:
When Trunch came in to bat, the bowlers tried to knock them flat;
Burningham said it wasn't fair, 'cos they got the runs off their underwear.
With those two great pals of mine, Albert Kipper and Douglas Sardyne.

Burningham batted nicely – scored 153 precisely;
With just one wicket falling, nothing could stop them scoring.
Sardyne was out of luck – run out for a duck –
Captain Albert Kipper grinned, and straightaway he turned to spin;
He got dizzy, what a shock – he threw the ball to Arthur Haddock!

Now Haddock was quite unfit, his hand had only two digits,
But though this was quite tragic, it made his bowling magic.
He sent one spinning down, the batsman played all round;
He raised his hand and cried 'Howzat?', but the umpire raised two fingers back.

Haddock was in heaven – he took 8 for 11 –
And Burningham were all done, for 171.
Haddock he was glad, but his team were hopping mad;
Now they had to go and face the Burningham boys terrible pace.
With those two great pals of mine, Albert Kipper and Douglas Sardyne.

Now Gilbert Silver-Darling found Larboard quite alarming.
He watched him mark his run-up, which nearly to the boundary come up;
The umpire he called 'Play', Larboard was on his way;
Like the very wind he sped – to ask the umpire what he'd said.
To save time he lobbed one down, and Gilbert hit it out of the ground.

I don't play cricket no more, because I reckon you ought to give the young ones a go. Not like Cyril Cockle – he refuse to give up playing, even though he have to bowl with a runner. Still, it's his ball, so no one can't do nothing about it. But I'm still a member of the TCCB (Trunch Cricket Club and Bar). As a matter of fact I've topped their drinking averages for the past four years, which is not to be sniffed up.

The match in this song took place in the final of the North Norfolk Tea Service in 1931. That was the biggest competition up our way – most of the others were just for a cup or a plate, or whatever, but this was for a whole tea service. Trunch had to play Burningham, 'cos they were the other team in the final, you see. They was known for their terrible fast bowlers. I don't mean they weren't any good – I mean they were terrible. In the previous round they had Mundesley 57 for 0, all retired hurt! So Trunch had this meeting and my Uncle Albert reckoned they should defend themselves by getting these Bodyline foundation garments off their wives – they were then made in a little factory in the village. So that's what they did. Of course those what din't have no wives had to get the undergarments off somebody else, but that's another story. Actually it's a more interesting story than this one, but my lips are sealed, which is more than you can say for Mrs Dace!

Now this raised Larboard's anger, so he made his run-up longer;
You can guess Gilbert's opinion, as he raced in from the pavilion.
But at the crease he stalled, and Larboard said 'No ball!' –
He'd left it in the pavilion, so the umpire lent him another one.
To save time he lobbed one down, and Gilbert hit it out of the ground.

Now Larboard he decided this was getting a bit one-sided,
So he walked back and he kept on, to the other side of Knapton.
But then, alas, alack, he couldn't find his way back;
They say he ran o'er dale and hill, and for all I know he's running still!
With those two great pals of mine, Albert Kipper and Douglas Sardyne.

Now to every wicked bouncer Trunch had the perfect answer,
As the batsmen neatly forced it off their reinforced Bodyline corsets.
Though some of them were out, to a CBW shout,
The rubber that those batsmen wore sent the next ball bouncing off for 4.
They got the runs, but so would you, the way those wicked bouncers flew!

So victory was completed, and Burningham was defeated;
Though Sardyne he was sour, it was Trunch's final hour.
Man of the Match, no doubt, leg byes – 140 not out.
Albert Kipper eased his stays, and said 'We won it by fair play';
Sardyne, he said 'No such thing – your lot had to cheat to win';
Captain Kipper clenched his fist, and said 'Bad losers make me sick';
Sardyne said did he mean him? – a fight broke out and we all joined in,
With those two great pals of mine, Albert Kipper and Douglas Sardyne,
Albert Kipper and Douglas Sardyne.

The Bonny Heavy Plough Horse

Oh my life it was ruined on that fateful day,
When the cruel recruiting sergeant came riding this way.
For he's done unto me two things most unkind:
Took away my bonny plough horse; left my husband behind.
For my bonny heavy plough horse to the war she has gone.

Oh I curse those cruel soldiers who tore us apart,
For my husband looks pathetic as he pulls the muck cart;
Why over the seas to fight strangers must they go,
When they could stay home and fight people they know?
But my bonny heavy plough horse, to the war she has gone.

Now news has come flying of where Dobbin has gone;
She fought at Balaclava with Cardigan on.
She charged like a plough horse, with a plough horse's knack –
Half a league onward, then half a league back.
Oh my bonny heavy plough horse, to the war she has gone.

On that field of battle up and down she did prance,
Till the enemy didn't know whether to retreat or advance,
They threw down their arms, oh they moaned and they groaned,
Crying 'If you won't fight fair, well, then we're going home.'
And my bonny heavy plough horse, the war she has won.

Today a battle-worn plough horse came over the heath,
With an old broken token held firm in her teeth;
With tears I did greet her, my joy I can't tell;
Of course it's not Dobbin, but it'll do just as well.
For a bonny heavy plough horse, from the war has come home.

In the old days people was always going off to war, leaving their loved ones behind to weep and mourn. Mostly it was the men what went, because people thought men were too weak to keep up the weeping and mourning for seven long years, which was how long you usually had to do it for. So they got the women to do that bit. In this case they all stayed to do the weeping and mourning, and sent the plough horse instead. Now plough horses used to be very important on farms. They were more important than the workers. I mean, the horses used to get fed every day, whether they needed it or not. They was always groomed with special brushes and combs, and hoovers (which were things for sucking the stones from horses' hooves). And the people in charge of the horses were called 'horsemen', for no good reason I can think of. These horsemen had to get up earlier than anyone else, to go and bait the horses. How that was done was a horseman's secret, but the idea was to bait the horses until they was really upset. Then, when they'd got them proper riled, they used to lead them out to the fields for the day's work. And I don't mean a day's work like what you get today. I mean a proper day's work. Nowadays people don't know what a day's work is. Well, I don't, anyhow.

The old horsemen had lots of secrets. Or, at least, they said they did. Of course, since they never told no one what they were it may all have been a bluff. But the sort of thing they had was like if you blew up a horse's nose that'd make it go better. As a matter of fact my cousin Kevin tried it once, with a couple of bangers, and it worked pretty well – though why anyone would want a horse to go backwards at that sort of speed I have no idea.

Now horses can be very intelligent. Farmer Trout, in our village, he used to have a horse that was bright as a mutton. If he went on his horse down to the Old Goat Inn – which is famous for being the lowest pub in England – he didn't have to worry about how much he drunk, because the horse could find its own way home, which meant old Trout could stay in the pub and have a few more, after the horse had gone. That was because of something called 'horse sense'. For instants, given the chance, horses would have more sense than to walk up and down main roads two abreast round blind bends – it's only the humans riding them what are that stupid. Most of all you'd think it made horse sense not to go racing each other around race courses, but that's where you'd be wrong. You see, horses are great gamblers. I mean, lambs are great gamblers too, but then they haven't got a lot to lose. But there's not a lot to bet on in the average meadow and not many other horses to bet with. At the races there's loads of other horses, and they can bet on things like how long it'll be before the women's hats blow off or how drunk their owners will get, so horses like going to the races. Except when they get shot, of course. Then they can't collect their winnings.

Years ago horses was a sign of wealth. People thought more of you if you rode a fine steaming stallion instead of a tatty old nag. Some posh people used to have horses for all occasions – hunters, polo ponies, draught horses, bottled horses – you name it and they had it. But like all these things it got out of hand and all sorts of people started to have fancy horses, and get above their stations. Mind you, that's all relative – I mean, you have to be pretty well off to own a station in the first place.

Of course, sooner or later a horse come to the end of it's working life. Like they say, enough is as good as a rest to a blind horse. But it's no good being soft about these things. A knackered horse have to be – well, knackered. As the other old saying goes: you can't flog a dead horse if the stable is bolted.

By the Cobblers

Valentino

In North Wal-sham, in the High Street, Where the shops all stand in line, By the
On the four-teenth, Feb-ru - a - ry, Came a par-cel tied with twine; Great sen-
Oh me dar-ling, oh me dar-ling, Oh me dar-ling Val - en - tine; You have

1.

cob-blers I was caught there, By a girl so sweet and fine;
- sa-tion, com-bin - a - tions, On the

2.3.

flap her name was
lost your coms for ev - er, Dread-ful sorr -ry, Val - en -

signed.
- tine.

In North Walsham, in the High Street,
Where the shops all stand in line,
By the cobblers I was caught there,
By a girl so sweet and fine;
On the fourteenth, February,
Came a parcel tied with twine;
Great sensation, combinations,
On the flap her name was signed.

Chorus
Oh me darling, oh me darling,
Oh me darling Valentine;
You have lost your coms forever,
Dreadful sorry, Valentine.

Red are Rose's, blue are Violet's
Pansy's pink and satin lined;
Daisy's white, well, no, not quite,
But they were once in their prime.
All these bloomers – not just rumours –
Have been offered many times;
Hers were cotton, from the bottom
Of her heart they said 'Be mine.'

So we planned to join our hands,
In the sunny summertime,
But the weather wasn't clever,
And my love she did decline.
How she wept, she wished she'd kept
Those things that kept her warm behind;
Without those she quickly froze,
And from exposure she did die.

At the grieving it was freezing,
In the bitter winter wynde.
So I donned her fleecy coms –
Of her love they me remind.
Now the thaw's on, summer draws on,
I can do without them fine,
So I love her little brother,
And forget my Valentine.

This was an old custom where people sent each other underwear instead of Valentine cards. The Coote
Memorial Museum are trying to revive it and they're asking people everywhere to send their underthings
so they can have an exhibition called 'Britain in Bloomers'. So please send your things to my cousin, Annie
Kipper, the curator – but not anytime near 14 February, or there could be some misunderstanding!

Combing the Mane

Teezi weezi

I sailed on a Yan-kee clip-per ship, With a hey, and a ho, to - geth-er; To the Bar-bar-y coast we took a trip, And is-'nt it aw-ful wea-ther? With man-y a close shave we sailed wide, We trimmed and set our sails be-side; Oh our suc-cess looked cut and dried; With a hey, and a ho, and a wash and go, As we combed the Span-ish Mane.

I sailed on a Yankee clipper ship,
With a hey and a ho, together;
To the Barbary coast we took a trip,
And isn't it awful weather?
With many a close shave we sailed wide,
We trimmed and set our sails beside;
Oh our success looked cut and dried;

Chorus
With a hey and a ho, and a wash and go,
As we combed the Spanish Mane.

There was Pigatail Pete and Razor Ruff,
With a hey and a ho, my wee friends;
There was young Al Opecia and old Dan Druff,
And anything for the weekend?
Our brave hands from none would cringe,
We teased the Dutch and the Celtic fringe,
And the King of Spain, his beard we singed;

Now our captain's name was Cut-throat Tarquin,
Hey, ho, blue bonnets,
We would have dyed any colour for him,
And would you like something on it?
The ugliest customer brought no fear,
From female cabin boy to old blue beard –
Until we met with a bald privateer;

'Ahoy,' he cried, 'You livery lot',
With a hey and a ho, brown trousers;
'An appointment now with me you've got,
And I'm ready for to do you now, Sir.'
We lowered our cutters and raised a froth,
His crew we cut with blades aloft,
And that bald privateer, we polished him off;

Now the Cut Above is our brigantyne,
With a hey and a ho, and a hey now;
She's the finest ship of the whole Hair Line,
And be sure and have a nice day now.
With magazines of the highest grade,
Without a fear we'll ply our trade,
Until the final parting's made;

This was one of Uncle Albert's favourite songs – well, it was till he went bald, anyhow. It's about a hairdressing ship like they had years ago to keep the tars jolly on them long trips. Sing it fast and it'll be over quicker.

Cool Yule

Tesco

Her - od looked out one win - ters day, and what do you think he spy?

Dressed in some old cur - tains, there came Three Wise Men by. They

called out "Mer - ry Christ - y - mas" and well, do you know what? Al -

- though the day was Christ - mas Day, Her - od had quite for - got.

But nev -er mind that, don't be a fool; Eat, drink, be mer -ry, and have a cool yule.

This is a song what was written by Rev. 'Call Me Derek' Bream. I did it on the 'Christmas Robin' tour with Mister Dave Burland, my 'Partner in Crime'. Some people say we go together like oil and cheese, but so what? That only mean we should go down well in Italy, don't it? The *Trunch Trumpet* done a review and said 'Dave's accompaniments are sensitive without being intrusive, while Sid's instrumental work is intrusive without being sensitive.' Sounds like the perfect match to me.

Partners in Crime: Dave Burland and Sid Kipper.

Herod looked out one winter's day and what do you think he spy?
Dressed in some old curtains, there came Three Wise Men by.
They called out 'Merry Christymas' and well, do you know what?
Although the day was Christmas Day, Herod had quite forgot.

Chorus
But never mind that, don't be a fool;
Eat, drink, be merry and have a cool yule.

The Mystic Magi came to lunch, they said they'd travelled far;
Astrologers they said they were, following the stars.
They said the stars foretold that day a special child was born,
'And this,' they said, 'shall be his sign – definitely Capricorn.'

Then they rode off until they found where the little babe was on view,
They crossed his parents' palm with gold, they gave him joss sticks too;
The Magi looked into their balls and then, to tell the truth,
When they saw what the future held these Soothsayers said 'Sooth!'

Then they went home a different way, the babe to Egypt fled,
But Herod didn't know that, so he said 'I want him dead'.
He said 'I'll kill all the little boys', and that's what he did do,
Despite the women who said, to be fair, he should kill the little girls too.

The story of that little boy is now known very well,
But the fate of those astrologers you never hear heard tell.
They took a short cut through the dunes – they thought they'd take a chance,
And there these wise old seers died, due to unforeseen circumstance.

So here's the moral of the tale, sing it throughout the land
If your mother is quite pure, untouched by human hand;
If you're born in a lowly barn, if God is on your side,
Then you'll live, if not, hard luck – for you infanticide.

Death or Glory Wassail

Was - sa - il, was - sail, all o - ver the town, We are all was - sail -ers of fame and re - nown; O - pen you door, and fill up our cup, Or we'll sing through your let -ter box Un - til you cough up.

Wassail, wassail, we know you're about,
Though you sit in the dark and pretend that you're
out.
If you're thinking of calling the police to give chase,
Just who do you think is singing the bass?

Chorus
Wassail, wassail, all over the town,
We are all wassailers of fame and renown;
Open your door, and fill up our cup,
Or we'll sing through your letter-box
Until you cough up.

Wassail, wassail, all over your garden;
If we've done any damage then we beg your pardon.
We're sorry to call upon you so late,
But we had to pick the lock on your gate.

Wassail, wassail, that you may believe
'Tis more blesséd to give than it is to receive.
The more that you give the more blesséd are you;
The more we receive the less damage we'll do.

Wassail, wassail, with a crisp ten pound note
We could all drink your health down at the Old Goat;
If you haven't a tenner two fivers will do;
If not things don't look very healthy for you.

Wassail, wassail, all over for now,
Now you've seen sense we will make no more row.
Peace be upon you, all at your repose,
And we'll come no more nigh you until the pubs close.

This is the song of the Trunch Special Wassail Squad (the SWS). They're a cracked unit of wassail singers who go round to houses where the people refuse to open the door to the normal wassailers. These people are usually what they call 'incomers'. I don't know why they call them that. I mean, they go out as often as they come in, so you might as well call them 'outgoers'. On the other hand a lot of them aren't very outgoing at all and they stay in their cottages, and don't answer the door, which is why we have to send the SWS around in the first place. So all in all I reckon it's best just to ignore them and then you won't have to call them anything at all.

The SWS go round with blacked-up faces and have their motto – 'Who Dares Sings' – on their cap badges, and all that. Their favourite song after this one is 'We Won't Go Till We Get Some'. They can get some out of even the most incoming people.

But the most important thing about the SWS is that they're all sweared to secrecy about their members. Nobody knows who they are – except themselves, of course. Otherwise they couldn't go round together due to not knowing if they was the right people. So obviously I can't tell you if I'm a member of it or not. Of course, if I wasn't a member I could tell you that. But as it is I'm afraid I'll have to leave you as ignorant as I found you.

The Dumpling Song

Iceni

Come all of you stout Nor-folk folk, And all the thin ones al - so, For we must fight a foe as big As ev - er, if not more so. For there's a threat we all must face, From Mas-sing-ham to Mund-ham; They are a most per - ni - cious race, These dread-ful folk from Lon-don. But Dump -lings all, no mat -ter what, Will al - ways be the ones on top.

Come all of you stout Norfolk folk,
And all the thin ones also,
For we must fight a foe as big
As ever, if not more so.
For there's a threat we all must face,
From Massingham to Mundham;
They are a most pernicious race,
These dreadful folk from London.

Chorus
But Dumplings all, no matter what,
Will always be the ones on top.

It is well known to Norfolk folk
That Londoners have rabies;
They talk a foreign language, and
They eat each others' babies.
They think all birds are sparras,
And the privy is a toilet;
They reckon Norfolk's all unspoilt,
So then they come and spoil it.

Now we keep hearing, on the news,
That London is so favoured;
If they believe that, well, I mean,
Why don't they all just stay there?
They come and live in all our barns,
Creating homeless hens,
Then insult all our women folk
By not seducing them.

It's not 'cos they complain like hell
When we go spreading muck;
It's just that they don't have the sense
To simply learn to duck.
It's not 'cos they are pale of skin,
While we are ruddy faced;
It's just that now they've bought it all
They think they own the place.

Now we won't burn their houses down,
For that would be a waste;
We won't attack them in the streets –
They don't like being chased.
That being so, then here's a way
To get what we are needing:
Let's turn them into Norfolk folk
By lots of interbreeding.

Gobblers in the Garden

Poultri

Oh when first I wed me Nor - folk girl we all went back to Trunch, To

drink a toast and cut the cake and have a bite of lunch. No - ow she and I were ea - ea - ger to

start the hon - ey - moon, But her fa - ther made a speech which went on half the af - ter - noon; He told me;

Treat me daugh - ter dec - ent, don't do her an - y ill, And when I go I'll leave you my small -

- hold - ing in me will, I'll leave me muck heap and me sil - age, me slu - rry and me swill, And

all the great big gob - blers in the gar - den.

This is a song about gobblers, which is an old Norfolk word for turkeys. Mind you, turkey was another old Norfolk word for turkey, but, you see, turkeys was very important in Norfolk at one time of the day. Well they still are today, as a matter of fact, but they're raised different. Years ago they used to keep them safe and warm in barns, and sell them fresh. Now they leave them out of doors and sell them frozen.

My Great Uncle Albert won a gold medal singing this song in the folk Olympics at the Old Goat Inn in 1921. Those were the days when folk-singing was a big thing and a gold medal was really something. They had all sorts of different events – ballad singing, chorus singing, things like that. Then there was how high you could sing, how long you could sing and how loud you could sing. That last one was the one Albert won. They used to have to stand up against this white line in Farmer Trout's meadow and sing as loud as they could. The blokes with the measuring tape started at the far end of the field and when they could hear the singer they stopped and measured the distance. They could hear Albert before they ever set off, so they went in the opposite direction till they couldn't hear him no more. Just to be certain they went on to Knapton and had a drink there, until they were sure he'd finished singing. It would have been a new record, except for the fact it was wind assisted. Of course, you can't do singing unless you're wind assisted, so all records were always disqualified. That way they never had to give away the barrel of beer which was on offer for a new record.

Oh when first I wed me Norfolk girl we all went back to Trunch,
To drink a toast and cut the cake and have a bite of lunch.
Now she and I were eager to start the honeymoon,
But her father made a speech which went on half the afternoon –
he told me:

Chorus
Treat me daughter decent, don't do her any ill,
And when I go I'll leave you my smallholding in me will,
I'll leave me muck heap and me silage, me slurry and me swill,
And all the great big gobblers in the garden.

When finally he finished my eyelids felt like lead,
So me and my new missus said we thought 'twas time for bed;
In the coach I said 'I thought we'd never get away from him',
But when we cuddled up the driver turned round with a grin,
And he said:

He drove us to our lodgings, and he said 'Cheerio',
But I finally made him realise it was him that ought to go;
And soon we lay together, my wife said 'Go to town',
But my ambition withered when the window pane flew down,
This voice said:

She said 'You've really got to laugh', but I was proper riled;
I was so fed up I couldn't even raise a smile;
I couldn't see the joke at all, all I saw was red,
For every time we kissed he called from underneath the bed,
And he said:

Now we've been married seven years and we've got three young pups;
Twice he went on holiday and once we tied him up!
And every hour of every day his promises we've heard;
Now me and my old twelve bore think it's time he kept his word –
His words are:

The Harvest Moan

Macaroni

We plough the fields and scatter the good seed on the land, But after that things never go in quite the way we planned; The moles and mice and magpies come down to eat the grain; Before a week is over we must scatter the seed again. All good things around us belong to someone else; With one accord we thank the Lord, and tighten up out belts.

We plough the fields and scatter the good seed on the land,
But after that things never go in quite the way we planned;
The moles and mice, and magpies come down to eat the grain;
Before a week is over we must scatter the seed again.

Chorus
All good things around us belong to someone else;
With one accord we thank the Lord and tighten up our belts.

This time some seeds are left to sprout and poke their young heads out;
They seem both hale and hearty, until we have a drought.
So with the sweat from off our brows we irrigate the crop,
Until at last the rain begins – and then it just won't stop.

But when the downpour ceases a few young plants remain;
The sun lifts up their heads and we begin to hope again.
To think that such fine healthy plants grew from such tiny seeds!
But on examination we find most of them are weeds.

What's left when we have weeded begins to turn to brown,
The time has come to harvest all that has not been blown down.
The yield is poor – in fact, there is just sufficient there
To plough the fields and scatter on the land again next year.

This song shows you how hard life was in the old days. That's one of the reasons why you'll never catch me doing no farming. You have to get up at the crack of dawn, when I'm usually going to bed. What I say is that early birds only catch worms and then they have to go to the doctor to get something for them. So, all in all, 'early to bed, early to rise' only means you have longer to wait till the pub opens and then you have to leave at closing time, just as things are getting going.

Mind you, I can remember the harvest in the old days. That was blooming hot work, which went on from dawn to dusk. Which make me wonder why they always held it in August, when the sun is shining and the days are long. You'd think that would make more sense to have it in November, when there's nothing else to do and you could knock off at four o'clock. I thought that was the whole idea of winter wheat. Still, August is the traditional time and you can't argue with tradition.

This song is about a small farmer, but they weren't the only sort. They used to come in all shapes and sizes. Some of them were so big that they couldn't bend down far enough to get their hands dirty. They was known as big landowners. Now in 1871 the big land owners got fed up with the Union of Sweedbashers and Allied Trades, and went on strike themselves to get their own back. They stayed out for forty-three years, and nobody noticed. They finally give it up in 1914, for patriotic reasons, due to the war. They all come back from their holiday homes in London and said what a pity it was they couldn't go and fight, due to them doing vital war work on their farms. Them coming back caused far more trouble than the strike, because the land owners had forgotten what it was they did – which was nothing – so they spent all their time wandering round getting in the way of people who were doing their jobs perfectly well, thank you.

Nowadays, of course, the landowners are even bigger, so you can't see them at all. There's a lot of land around Southrepps way owned by some bloke called Coalboard Pension-Fund, but no one has ever clapped eyes on him. But no matter – that still gets set aside perfectly well without him. Which bring me to another thing. This here set-aside is much more my sort of farming. You have to agree not to do any actual farming and then they send you money. Of course, if you'd rather you can carry on farming and they'll send you money for that instead. It's all to do with the EEC, which stands for just about anything you like as far as I can see. They're a sort of a charity which is biased in Brussels, although strangely enough the only thing you can't get grants for is sprouts, which you might think they'd be rather keen on. But don't just take my word for it about farmers. Take these words, from another old song, 'The Farmer's Crumpet':

I can cook, I can sew, I can sweep and knead dough,
And at dances I am a real charmer;
But jolly girls all, pay heed to my call,
God help you if you marry a farmer!

Hay! Do The Morris

Here's a dance that's easy to do,
And it'll make you fertile too.
With breeches white and a hat from the florist,
Now get ready to do the morris.

Chorus
Hay! Do the morris dance.
Hay! Let's process and prance:
Up and down, and round and round,
Until you fall down on the ground.

Pick your bells and sticks up quick,
'Cos now we're going to get rustic;
Get some drunks to play a tune,
And you'll be morris dancing soon.

Tuck your trousers in your socks,
Grow a beard and wear a smock;
Drink till you can hardly stand,
And now you are a morris man.

Now a fool we will need too –
Any one of you will do.
Let him be nimble, let him be quick,
Let him wave his bladder on a stick.

First you take your hanky out,
Put it in, then shake it about;
Hit each other with your sticks,
And that is all there is to it.

While you take part in this frolic
Remember that it's all symbolic.
You'll bless the crops and speed the plough,
And all by jumping up and down.

Every new dance craze have a song what go with it and that was as true in the old days as it is today. Which means it's only true today if it was true in the old days, which it was, like I said. Now there was lots of these old songs – things like 'Let's Gavotte Again, Like We Did Last Autumn' and 'When You Finish the Finnish'. But with the dances having died out you don't hear the songs no more.

This song is the one what started the morris-dancing craze. It does tend to upset some morris dancers, mainly due to the first line of the song. Some of them can turn quite ugly. Some can't, of course, due to being quite ugly to start with. Mind you, I can't see why – I mean, it looks easy enough to me, even if some of them do manage to make it look difficult!

I often think there must be more to morris dancing than morris dancing – I mean, otherwise why would grown people do it? Take Trunch Morris. They're what they call a mixed side – that mean that some of them aren't much good and the rest are totally useless. The sort of morris dancing they do is called south-east morris, which is done in carpet slippers and gingham. What they do in the summer is that every Wednesday night they go out and dance at some pub where they're welcome. Which means over the years they've travelled further and further afield. You often see them setting out on a Tuesday these days. But in the winter they lock themselves in the village hall every Wednesday. And if you ask them what they're doing they say they're practising. Which sounds fair enough, till you see them when they come out again the next spring, 'cos they're no better than they were when they went in. So I think there's something else going on and I wonder if it's something to do with them masons? I mean, that would explain the funny costumes and the strange behaviour, wouldn't it?

Sid being pursued by The Witchmen, after expressing his views on morris dancing.

41

The Innocent Dodo

I prithee good Ladies and Lordies attend;
Give ear to my sorrowful ode-oh.
By means of this ballad I now do intend
To sing you in praise of the dodo.
In far off Mauritia the dodo do dwell,
Halfway to the far Antipode-oh;
And if we would serve her, then this I must tell:
It should not be parboiled, a la mode-oh.
For if the poor creature is but to keep going,
Our slogan must be 'Stop the Bloody Dodoing.'

The dodo in the morning she falls from her nest –
If she could she would surely have flowed-oh
She returns in the evening to take her sweet rest,
Though how she ascends I am blowed-oh.
And all in her season she'll go with her mates,
By them she will soon be bestrode-oh.

And as she may dally with seven or eight,
Then 'tis clear that she risks overload–oh.
And as she must put up with all of this stuff,
I ask dost thou not think she's suffered enough?

How many roads must a dodo walk down
Before you can call her a dodo?
How many seas must a white dodo sail
Before she can sleep in the road–oh?
Ripe fruit and berries, and nuts that are nigh,
In the bird's stomach are stowed–oh;
Be grateful, good people, the dodo don't fly,
For 'twould danger you when she unload–oh.
And if you should question on what she had dined,
The answer, my friend, would be blowing in the
wynde.
And so on my tunic this message I spell;
'God Save the King, and the Dodo as Well.'

42

Jack Onion

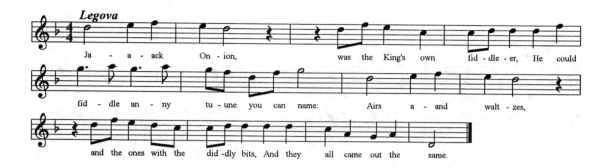

Jack Onion was the King's own fiddler,
He could fiddle any tune you can name:
Airs and waltzes, and the ones with the diddly bits,
And they all came out the same.

When he played he could break your heart;
He could scare the birds into the trees.
He would play your favourite tunes,
Despite your loudest pleas.

In the Great Hall, all the Ladies and Lords,
Gathered for a big do;
Jack Onion came to play for them,
Though no one asked him to.

He played so long, so loud and strong,
The very air itself was cleft;
They were all movéd, clean out of the room –
Except the King's own daughter deaf.

Her eyes were blue, her lips were red,
Her hair was of the darkest black;
It tumbled down to her milk-white shoulder,
But she caught it and put it back.

'Oh,' she cried, 'when I watch you fiddle
Each part and movement I adore;
You must come, and perform with me,
The finest piece ever scored.'

So late that night he went to her room,
After her maids had left her all alone;
What a sight met Jack Onion's eyes –
She wore nothing but a sousaphone.

How they played, for the whole of the night,
Such music as no one ever knew;
Like a demon he fiddled in and out,
While the Princess puffed, and blew.

Then, out cried the King's daughter deaf;
'I think I feel the cock to crow.
If my father should find you here,
He'd see you were well hung, I know.'

As she spoke the door flew wide
And there in his night-mail stood the King;
Crying 'Jack Onion, you must forfeit your life,
Or stop that awful din.'

Jack Onion jumpéd up to his knees,
Crying 'Grant me nought but mine own life;
I ask no more, except perhaps some land,
And – oh yes – your daughter for my wife.'

'For your boldness you may keep your life,
And have my own deaf daughter dear.
And I will grant you your own estates,
A long, long way from here.'

Now Jack Onion is a noble Lord,
With servants all at his command.
And often he fiddles with the King's dear daughter,
As she sits on his right hand.

Jam Tomorrow

Verdi

Now-a-days it's the rage to be E-co; You laugh but, I'm not nuts, my pis-ta-ch-io. To be seen to be green is my pas-sion; My life-style is worth-while, but so in fash-ion. Whole-meal bread, low fat spread, fil-tered wa-ter; Full of beans, no caf-fein, like you ought-a; Eat brown rice, aw-fully nice, me-oh-my-o, Check the tins for nas-ty things when you buy-o.

Nowadays it's the rage to be Eco;
You laugh but, I'm not nuts, my pistachio.
To be seen to be green is my passion;
My life-style is worthwhile, but so in fashion.

Chorus
Wholemeal bread, low fat spread, filtered water;
Full of beans, no caffeine, like you oughta;
Eat brown rice, awfully nice, me-oh-my-o,
Check the tins for nasty things when you buy-o.

Off you go, deux chevaux, on condition
That you be quite lead-free in your emissions.
On your bike, if you like, but what sorrow:
Motorway, new today, jammed tomorrow.

Take no pills for your ills at any juncture;
Just say no and then go for acupuncture.
It's all done for our sons and our daughters;
Friend of the earth, I give birth underwater.

You can't fail with real ale, it's tradition.
But it should be alcohol free in addition.
A glass of wine, that's just fine, it won't pain yer;
I happen to know a good Bordeaux from Albania.

Now I own a second home up in Norfolk,
Where I spend my weekends among the poor
folk.
They admire their new squire and they know it;
Yes they know, though they don't always show it.

I'm so green, as you've seen from this recital.
In my trade it's been made really vital.
Shopping malls I install, don't you scoff it:
Son of a bitch I'll get rich on the profit.

(By Derek Bream and Kevin Kipper)

44

Knock Down, Knock Down for Jesus

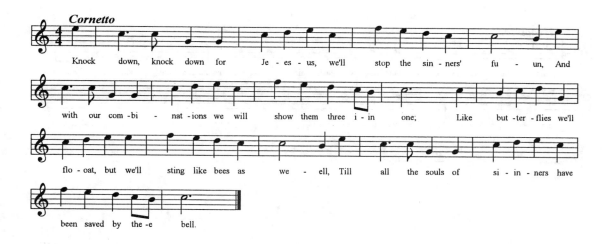

Cornetto

Knock down, knock down for Je - es - us, we'll stop the sin - ners' fu - un, And
with our com - bi - nat - ions we will show them three i - in one; Like but -ter -flies we'll
flo - oat, but we'll sting like bees as we - ell, Till all the souls of si - in - ners have
been saved by the -e bell.

Knock down, knock down for Jesus, we'll stop the sinners' fun,
And with our combinations we will show them three in one;
Like butterflies we'll float, but we'll sting like bees as well,
Till all the souls of sinners have been saved by the bell.

We'll march unto the alehouse, where Courage we will take;
If hearts we wish to conquer, then heads we first must break.
From Knapton up to Sheringham we'll fight from town to town;
Before the dead can rise up, we must knock the living down.

We'll dig up all the hatchets, turn ploughshares into swords,
For sticks and stones will break their bones, so why waste breath on words?
With palms we'll raise hosannas, with knuckles we'll raise lumps;
And if they turn the other cheek, the other cheek we'll thump.

Now with our Bible boots on we will march for all we're worth,
For if it's left to them alone the meek would lose the earth.
Let every day be Boxing Day, we'll win the dialogue,
All with the cross of Jesus and the uppercut of God.

But rest not on your laurels – there's more that must be done
The fight will not be over till the Bible belt is won.
Gird on the gloves of glory, slough off the shirt of sin,
Pull on the gospel jock strap, till all is gathered in.

This is the song of the Boxing Booths who was a militant branch of the Salvation Army. They used to go about beating people up for Jesus. They went from street to street, knocking on people's faces – it was called the 'laying on of hands', I think. Anyhow, they were never very successful, due to having an awful band. Well, you try playing the trumpet with boxing gloves on. They was made illegal some years ago, but even that couldn't make them popular, so you never get them about nowadays.

Lord Hardwick

Lord Hard-wick he a - hunt-ing went, with his hawk and his hounds and all, And al-
-ong with him went his two foot sol-diers, twen-ty-four in - ches tall, Just
twen-ty-four in-ches tall.

A bloke once asked me why all these long boring ballads are about Lords and Ladies, and the like. So I told him – mind your own business. But there is a reason for it. You see, in the old days it was Ladies and Lords, and the like, what lived long boring lives. Ordinary people, like I used to be, used to live short boring lives – with choruses, as often as not.

Now this ballad is not just long and boring; it's also about a subject no one is interested in no more. What I'm on about is maidenheads. Years ago, if the songs are anything to go by, they thought of little else. Of course nobody keeps maidenheads any more because they're too much trouble. But what I can't work out is if these maidenheads were so valuable, how come in all the songs they were always going out and losing them? Why din't they leave them at home where they'd be safe?

This song also have another title, but I don't use that no more. The other title is 'The Cunning Stunt', but like I say, I don't use it. Not since Taunton. As a matter of fact I'll probably never work in Taunton again. So, if you're gong to sing this song, take my advice and call it Lord Hardwick. I mean, nobody minds if you say Hord Lardwick, do they?

By the way, I hope you don't mind if this song is about hunting, because it is. Years ago people din't know any better. Today, of course, everyone is all against it. Today even I'm against it. Yesterday I wasn't and tomorrow I may not be too sure, but today I'm all against it. The thing is, hunting's too dangerous today. Only this very morning Lord Silver-Darling had an anonymous death threat from the anti-hunt people. Now I think that's getting a bit daft. I mean, what's the point of anonymous death threats? I reckon you definitely ought to say who you're going to kill.

So, nowadays people don't have hawks and hounds, and all. Nowadays people have dogs just for the company. So posh people like Lords and Ladies have posh dogs, with long pedigrees due to inbreeding, which I won't go into, on account of it always upsets my Auntie Marion. They're all members of the Kennel Club – that's a place where all the waitresses dress up with big ears and waggy tails, and not much else – where they go to talk about the good old days when they was allowed to hunt.

But the hunt wasn't all bad. They din't always hunt poor innocent creatures, like in this song Sometimes they used to have a drag hunt instead. That was where all the men used to dress up as women, and likewise. They used to say that if you hadn't seen all them men riding side-saddle in full skirts you hadn't lived. Mind you, my grandfather never saw it and if he didn't live, how did I get here?

Lord Hardwick he a-hunting went, with his hawk and his hounds, and all;
And along with him sent his two foot soldiers, twenty-four inches tall, just twenty-four inches tall.

They looked low, and he looked high, with his broadsword in his hand;
Each nook and cranny they did search, they beat the bushes round, but no game could be found.

And as he crossed the river wide, with his hawk and his hounds, and all,
He rode high above the tide, while his two foot soldiers swore – it was three foot deep or more.

And when he reached the further bank, with his broadsword in his hand,
He saw a maiden bathing there – she looked just like a swan, but with no feathers on.

Lord Hardwick he did stop and stare, for clothes were all she lacked;
And Cupid's arrow piercéd him – he lost his heart, alack, when she swum on her back.

Lord Hardwick he did stop and stare, with his broadsword in his hand;
His spaniel it did prick it's ears, and his pointer it did stand.

Well now this maid swam to the bank, she stepped ashore with ease;
He dried her body with his cloak, while the soldiers dried her knees – that was all that they could reach.

Said he 'Fair maid, pray tell to me, what is your father's name?'
'Oh my father's name is Partridge' – said he 'And are you game?'

'Oh sir, I fear you startle me, with your broadsword in your hand;
I am but a poor maiden, and you a well-endowed man, with a bulging purse, and land.'

Said he 'Fair maid pray say that I may have your maidenhead;
Just say I may and I will give you half my purse,' he said, 'or an equal prize instead.'

'Then I pledge to you my maidenhead, and I'll take half your purse;
Oh now my maidenhead is yours – the deal can't be reversed – but you must find it first.'

Lord Hardwick thought the bargain fair, with his hawk and his hounds, and all;
To the searching for her maidenhead his soldiers he did call, though their interest was small.

Then how she laughed, how she scoffed, at his hawk, his hounds, and all;
'The thing that you have bought so dear, I lost it on a horse, while riding in the gorse.'

'So now that horse belongs to you, and half your purse is mine;
Now that horse belongs to you, so ride, you beggar, ride, and I hope you're satisfied.'

He cursed high, his soldiers cursed low, for the spoiling of their hunt,
And the maid she went off laughing for she'd fooled them back to front, it was such a cunning stunt.

And with the purse that she had won her own true love she wed;
They happy were and all because, no matter what was said, this maiden used her head.

Love Divining

Lustfully

When I was sev-en-teen years old I wan-ted to be wed-ded:

Be he fair, or be he dark, or be he quite bald head-ed. I

peeled an ap-ple all in one, my man's name to an-nounce; I

threw the peel; if that's his name, it's one I can't pro-nounce.

Tom, Dick or Har-ry, Ni-gel or Ned,

Mat--thew, Mark or Luke or John; oh which one will I wed?

This song is all about divining. Years ago people used to do divining to try and find out who they was going to marry. I can't see the point of it, really. I mean, if you're definitely going to marry them then you'll find out in due course anyhow. Plus that can lead to disappointment. Take Maureen Moray. She made a special cake and ate it and went to sleep, and she had a perfect view of the bloke she was going to marry. She woke up knowing exactly what he looked like. The only trouble is she's never met anyone who looked like that. She's still looking, but as that was over 50 years ago now I expect he's changed a bit.

You see, years ago, people used to be superstitious. That meant they believed in signs and poor tents, and things like that. Take fishermen. Now, due to the fact that they never knew whether they was going to catch any fish or not, fishermen was very superstitious – you might say they was super superstitious. Some people say they was superduper superstitious, but that's just being stupid. Anyhow, they had all these things about whether it was lucky to put to sea or not. One place I know they won't put out if they see a rabbit on the way to the boat – which is a bit of bad luck, 'cos the way they go to the boats runs through all these fields and woods which are full of rabbits. Mind you, they don't have to go that way. They live right next to the harbour, as a matter of fact, but that's the traditional way to go and of course it'd be bad luck to break the tradition. It's like touching wood and avoiding the cracks in the pavement, and not walking under ladders. They don't really work. I know, 'cos my Uncle Walter tried them all. In fact, it was the end of him. He was so busy concentrating on doing them all that he dropped his lucky heather in the road and got run over picking it up again.

Of course, now I'm appearing in theatres and things there's a whole new lot of luck to learn. There's breaking a leg while not whistling and things like that. And then there's not mentioning some play which I've forgotten, which is a bit worrying 'cos I might remember it but forget the not mentioning it bit and mention it by accident. That'd be just my luck.

When I was seventeen years old I wanted to be wedded –
Be he fair, or be he dark, or be he quite bald headed.
I peeled an apple all in one, my man's name to announce;
I threw the peel: if that's his name, it's one I can't pronounce.

Chorus
Tom, Dick or Harry, Nigel, or Ned,
Matthew, Mark or Luke or John, oh which one will I wed?

Then came my eighteenth birthday, and still none had made his claim,
So I put some nuts around the fire, and each one had a name;
I put some nuts around the fire, and gave them my appraisal,
The first to burst should be my love – it seems I'll marry Hazel.

By nineteen I was wondering if I would wed at all,
So I went to the gypsy, and she gazed into her ball.
I said I feared a single life, she said there is no danger –
He'll be tall and dark and handsome, and they won't come any stranger.

At twenty years of age my blushing groom had still not come,
So the cherry stones I counted, all to find my own true one;
The cherry stones I counted, and they said he'd be a tinker;
Now any man that tinks with me, I'm his – hook, line, and sinker.

Well last week I passed twenty-one, and so I hoped no more
To ever meet the one who had the key to fit my door.
But in my bed last night my long-awaited love he came;
He lies there gently snoring, and I still don't know his name!

The Mild Rover

Sirocco forte

I've been a mild ro-ver for man-y's a year, And I've spent all my
mon-ey on warm gin-ger beer. But now I am turn-ing, like worms have be-
-fore, And I nev-er will play the mild ro-ver no more, And it's no,
nay, nev-er; no nay nev-er no more, Will I
play the mild ro-ver, no ne-ver no
more.

I've been a mild rover for many's a year,
And I've spent all my money on warm ginger beer.
But now I am turning, like worms have before,
And I never will play the mild rover no more.

Chorus
And it's no, nay, never, no nay never no more,
Will I play the mild rover, no never no more.

I went into an alehouse I used to frequent,
And I told the landlady me money was spent;
I asked her for credit, she answered me 'Yes –
I've seen this done before, now get out your
largesse.'

I put me hand in me pocket, pulled out what I'd got,
And the landlady's eyes opened wide with the shock.
She said 'Where's the money?' – 'But I thought you
knew:
I told you I'd none in verse one and verse two.'

I'll go home to my family, tell them what I did,
And ask them to lend me a couple of quid.
For I can see clear that I've misspent my youth,
From now on I'll be jolly rough and uncooth.

Now I'll go wild, to the pub I will stray –
If they ask me to leave I won't go straight away:
I'll stay up past my bedtime, get loose women tight,
I will be a wild rover – well, I think, p'rhaps, I might.

In my little village of St Just, Friday night is 'women's quiet night in'. They absolutely insist on it. So at about eight o'clock on a Friday you'll see all the men wandering around, having been thrown out of the house. Well there's only two places open on a Friday night and they'd look a bit stupid at the junior youth club in the village hall, so they all get in the Old Goat Inn. Well, if you go in the pub you have to have a drink, so they sip them as slow as they can until it's time to go home. But Ernie Spratt, the landlord, have worked all this out and he keep putting the clock back. So just as they finish their pint they look at the clock and realise they can't go as yet. So then they have to order another one. This goes on till about half-past three, when Ernie gets fed up and want's to go to bed, so he lets them go. They stagger home, accidentally the worse for wear, and then they get in trouble. It's a tough life, I can tell you. Anyhow, this is one of the songs they sing on the way home, to get their courage up.

The Muntons of Moorgate

Vinegretto

Oh Mar-tha this Knap-ton's a quite fright-ful sight, There's no-thing much hap-pens by day or by night. There is-n't a street lamp in all of the town, And they're dig-ging for what they call 'spuds' in the ground. It looked aw-fully sim-ple, des-pite all the mud, So I gave them a hand at this dig-ging for 'spuds'; Now my ach-ing back makes me wish I could stand, Where the Char-ing Cross Ro-oad sweeps down to the Strand.

Oh Martha this Knapton's a quite frightful sight,
There's nothing much happens by day or by night.
There isn't a street lamp in all of the town,
And they're digging for what they call 'spuds' in the
ground.
It looked awfully simple, despite all the mud,
So I gave them a hand at this digging for 'spuds':
Now my aching back makes me wish I could stand,
Where the Charing Cross Road sweeps down to the
Strand.

You remember Judge Jenkins from Mayfair, of course,
Well I saw him today dangling under a horse.
I asked if the rider should not be on top,
And he promised to try that, if he could get it to stop.
So while we tried halting this nag in its path,
The whole population stopped working to laugh;
For such disrespect he would see them all hanged,
Where the Charing Cross Road sweeps down to the
Strand.

Now some of the girls here, one does have to say,
Are quite striking, in a naïve sort of way.
I met one today who had me discomposed –
She painted a picture with cheeks like a rose.
But when at those roses I ventured to sip,
I found she'd used gloss and she stuck to my lip.
Now we live cheek by jowl – well, they'd not under-
stand
Where the Charing Cross Road sweeps down to the
Strand.

So Martha this letter must serve to explain
That I'll soon be returning to London again.
My nights are all spent in the counting of sheep,
Then the birds wake me up just as I get to sleep.
The views are too roomy, the people ill-dressed,
And the air from the pigsties is simply too fresh;
I can't wait for the fog that comes rolling so grand,
Where the Charing Cross Road sweeps down to the
Strand.

51

Murder at the Red Barndance

Scarlatti

When the Red Barn was used for the danc-ing, There was one that stood out from the rest; Sweet six-teen year old Fan-ny Fan-tail, At her first dance, and in her best dress. She knew that a maid must be caut-ious; She knew not to trust men, bec - ause She knew one thing led to the oth - er, But she did-n't know which thing it was!

When the Red Barn was used for the dancing,
There was one that stood out from the rest;
Sweet sixteen-year-old Fanny Fantail,
At her first dance, and in her best dress.
She knew that a maid must be cautious;
She knew not to trust men, because
She knew one thing led to the other,
But she didn't know which thing it was!

When Dick Dace asked her to polka
She blushed from her head to her toes,
Though naturally Dick couldn't see that,
'Cos she was still wearing her clothes.
They danced the Dashing White Privates,
They danced all the two-steps and threes;
They danced in Sir Cassion's circle,
Till Sir Cassion gave at the knees.

They danced out the door to the moonlight,
For the night was not rainy nor cold;
Oh how she admired his hornpipe,
And he praised her ballroom hold.

In the Red Barn the others kept dancing,
Till all of a sudden they froze:
'Twas the worst scream that any remembered
Since Jack danced on Abigail's toes.

There on the steps lay the body
Stabbed through the heart, with an axe;
The blood spurted on to the paving,
And then it ran into the cracks.
Still holding the bloody weapon
Stood the flaming killer, who spake:
'Before we go any further,
I've got a confession to make.'

'Oh I just could not stand to be spurned so,
As we went for our moonlit walk;
For intercourse I had been promised,
But then he just wanted to talk.'
So, all you young Dicks, mind the Fannys;
The moral should now be quite clear:
Though you may have decent intentions
She may have a better idea!

This is a true story about what happened at a dance held by the Union of Sweedbashers and Allied Trades, many years ago. It's the sort of local song what you get in different parts of the country, which are of no interest to anyone else, really. Unless you like sex and violence, of course.

There's a lot of different versions of this song. In some versions the girl is called Frances, or even Genevieve, and the bloke is called Virgil. In some versions nobody murders nobody, and they all live happily ever after, except for the vicar, who gets a nasty cold. Sometimes it isn't a dance at all, but a cheese and wine party, and the murder happens the other way round. There's even a version in which none of the things what happen in this version happen at all. That one is called 'The Ash Grove'. But, like I say, apart from that this is a real true story about what actually happened.

As you can see from this song, crime isn't what it used to be. I mean, crime is terrible in St Just nowadays – you can't get away with nothing! It's all due to this new policeman what we've got – PC Chubb. He's a proper sticker, he is. Only the other month he done Cyril Cockle for wasting police time. Cyril said he hadn't done nothing wrong, but old Chubb said 'Exactly!' He said he'd been following him for two hours, so he'd been wasting his time. Cyril got a fine for that. Now we aren't used to that sort of thing. We're used to the old-fashioned Bobby on the beat. Years ago we used to have a bloke called Constable Crabb. Now he was a proper sort of a policeman. If you was in the Old Goat Inn at closing time you'd see Ernie Spratt, the landlord, look across at Crabb and Crabb'd say 'That's alright, Ernie, you keep on serving – there can't be nothing going wrong if I'm here, can there?' And as long as he got a couple of pints for his evidence, then that was alright. It was the same with the poaching – he used to come with me and my uncle George. He used to say 'There can't be nothing wrong if I'm here, can there?' And as long as he got a couple of pheasants for his evidence, then that was alright. But we lost him, a while back. Well, we didn't lose him – we know where he went. He went up in smoke at the crematorium as a matter of fact. He was shot dead in a bank raid in North Walsham. Tragic it was. He was just loading the evidence into his bag at the time.

Cyril Cockle wasting his own time in Cromer.

Old, Waily, Windy Knight

'Oh me head it is frozen to me hat,
The snow is drifting down me back,
I fear I will die of cold in fact,
All in this biting wind-oh.'

Chorus
'Let me in,' Sir Jasper cried,
Old, waily, windy knight.
'Let me in,' Sir Jasper cried,
'Here beneath your window.'

The window it has opened wide,
This ploughboy's stuck his head outside,
He said 'You're really not my type;
You should try my sister Linda.'

Now he's found the window where she snores,
But it was on the second floor,
So he's thrown pebbles, two, three, four,
And the glass rained down on him-oh.

Then up a ladder he has climbed,
And to her window come, betimes,
He's tapped on it seven times,
Calling 'Open up your window.'

'Oh that I will then,' Linda cried,
And she has thrown her window wide,
But it has knocked the ladder aside,
And he's dangling by his fingers.

Despite that wicked wind so chill
He's hauled himself up with a will;
If it weren't for the ice upon the sill
He would surely have got in-oh.

But down he's tumbled to the ground,
And there the broken glass he's found,
And he has made a fearful sound,
Outside her grandma's window.

Well grandma's opened her window wide
To find this winded knight outside,
And she has blessed the Lord on high,
And she has pulled him in-oh.

She's catched the window with a grin,
And she has kissed him cheek and chin,
She's slipped in between the sheets with him,
For he's frozen stiff, poor thing-oh.

'Let me out,' Sir Jasper cried,
Old, waily, windy knight.
'Let me out,' Sir Jasper cried,
But she opened and she took him in-oh.

Prince of Whales

Now I'll sing you a whaling song
(Heave up, me boys, heave away);
And I'll keep on wailing 'cos whaling's wrong
(God bless the Prince of Whales).

The blue whale is the prince of fish
Me boys and me girls let's all sing this

That whale is blue as a blue lagoon
Well, you'd be blue if you was harpooned

I'm talking 'bout whales in the sea, you twit
Not a place full of daffodils and rarebit

God's creatures mustn't be chased and killed
Unless they happen to be krill

Now I am green, the whales are blue
They are big and cuddly too

Now catching whales is very bad
It's far, far worse than catching crabs

You can poison slugs, spray greenfly,
Eat live yoghurt, but whales mustn't die

Now whales are intelligent, but
If they're so clever why don't they duck?

So I've sung you a wailing song
Oh I'll stop wailing, I've gone on too long.

(Words and music by Derek Bream.)

Derek is very green. He has a 'Save the Soul' sticker in the back of his car and he's a member of Green Peas, which is some sort of group in favour of orgiastic vegetables, or something. He tries to get the farmers round here to stop spraying their crops, but, like they say, there aren't no lavatories out in the fields.

Now years ago people thought that whales was just big fish. They din't know that whales was as clever as the next man, and how they sang and all that. They just knew you needed a blooming great hook to catch one. You see, if whales are people, then that makes all the older people in the village cannibals, 'cos they ate a lot of whale meat during the last war. Anyhow, my Uncle Albert always reckoned the whales enjoyed the chase. And another thing. Just because whales are intelligent, it don't mean they're all friendly and peaceful. I mean, the most friendly and peaceful person in my village is thick as two short straws, and whales is no different. There's all sorts of whales. There's good whales and bad whales, and there's whales just like you and me, who just want to be left alone to get on with their lives, and have a few pints on a Saturday night.

Now a lot of people, as I go about, ask me how I stand on this sort of thing – being a famous megostar like I am. Actually, I tend to sit on the fence, 'cos that's a lot more restful than standing. On the other hand, I have to say that after doing this song a few times for the vicar it's persuaded me. I shan't go whaling off Cromer Pier ever again.

Queensbury Rules, OK

A story I'll sing and a song I will tell
Of two of the finest fist fighters;
Lord Cedric Smythe was a bit of a swell,
Fred Cod was a scruffy young blighter.
Now Fred he was rough, and Cedric was tough,
And both were but partially baked;
And so they were matched for some fine fisticuffs,
With the Lonsdale Braces at stake.

Chorus
And sing out Hurrah! Sing out Hurray!
They may have been stupid,
But still they were brave.

Before very long they stood in the ring,
The referee bid them shake hands.
And then they shook legs, the crowd all joined in,
And a fine hokey cokey began.
'You must strip to the waist,' the referee said,
And the ladies all cried out 'Hello!'
For Fred wasn't clear on the rules to be played,
So he stripped to the waist from below.

For round after round they danced round the ring
Till it seemed they'd been always *in situ*;
'Was there ever such sport,' Lord Cedric did sing,
Said Fred 'Just stand still while I hit you.'

Lord Cedric was getting on top of his man,
Which breaks every rule as we know it;
He gave Fred a belt that should have been banned,
So Fred promptly hit him below it.

The Lord was laid out, Fred was all set to win –
That blow it must surely decide it.
But then Cedric's second he threw the towel in,
With a blooming great brick wrapped inside it.
That brick it flew high, that brick it flew wide,
That brick it flew handsome I'd say;
Clean out of the ring that brick would have flied –
If Fred hadn't been in the way.

So now these two fighters lay flat on the deck
Like a couple of fish on a shelf.
The referee puzzled, then thought 'What the heck?'
And awarded the fight to himself.
And so in conclusion let's toss off a snort
To those battling bruisers of yore.
We'll drink to their health and to this happy thought –
We won't see their like any more.

This song is about Pry's fighting, which was a sort of fighting which was invented by a bloke called Mr Pry. The fighters used to fight for a purse. Of course, nowadays men don't carry purses, but in those days you had all these big, strong boxers going round with lots of purses they'd won and nothing to put in any of them. They never thought of asking for money instead. Or if they did they soon forgot about it after they'd been hit a few times. Mind you, it's swines and roustabouts really, 'cos if they'd asked for money instead they'd have had no purse to put it in.

I had a relation who was a boxer. That was 'Gripper' Kipper. He was the last of the bare-knuckle fighters. He give it up when they invented knuckle dusters – well, he had to, 'cos they killed him. 'Gripper' used to get up at the fairground and challenge people to fight him. This was very popular because 'Gripper' had a glass jaw.

The greatest hour that 'Gripper' had was at about half-past three one Tuesday afternoon, when he fought 'Keith' Pearshouse (he always had them marks around the Keith, even though it was his real name, because he reckoned everyone else had a nickname but him, so he made his real name his nickname. Which was a bit confusing. But not as confusing as if his real name had been Nick, I suppose). Anyhow, they fought for the championship of Ordnance Survey map 38 – North-east Norfolk. They used to decide the areas that way because it saved a lot of arguments – plus, if you was involved in local boxing you only had to buy the one map to find your way to the fights. They met in North Walsham market-place. They also met on Cromer promenade. Then they ran into each other on the cliffs at Overstrand. In fact, by the time the fight come round they were really quite good mates. So they shook hands and the referee said he wanted a dirty fight and to come out kicking, and they started off. Only they'd become such good friends that neither could bring himself to hit the other. After 147 rounds the referee said it was a tie so far and the first one to answer the elimination question would be the winner. So he opened the envelope and asked 'What is the capital of Norfolk?' Quick as a flush 'Gripper' said 'N' was the capital of Norfolk, while 'Keith' who was a bit hard of hearing said 'No – Watton isn't the capital of Norfolk.' The referee said they was both wrong, so they beat him up and went home. Which is why, to this very day, there is no current champion of Ordnance Survey map 38, 'cos there was no winner for them to challenge. Which may be just as well, 'cos they renumbered the maps, and map number 38 now covers Aberdeen, which is a hell of a long way to go to get beaten up.

Rolling Drunk

As I come out this morning my missus she proclaim; "Remember how you said last week you'd never drink again"? If she thought that I'd remember, another thought she should have thunk; It's Friday night, and I think I might get ro-o-o-lling drunk. Rolling drunk, we wi-ill get rol-liing drunk, We wi-ill get ro-o-lling, ro-o-li-ing, we will get ro-o-li-ing drunk.

As I come out this evening my missus she proclaim:
'Remember how you said last week you'd never drink again?'
If she thought that I'd remember, another thought she should have thunk;
It's Friday night, and I think I might get rolling drunk.

Chorus
Rolling drunk, we will get rolling drunk,
We will get rolling, rolling, we will get rolling drunk.

Now some of us like cider and some prefer the porter;
Some they have their whisky neat, and some with soda water.
Add all them somes together and the answer you can't flunk –
You'll have too much, and carry one home rolling drunk.

Bartholomew has never smoked a fag in all his life;
He only eats raw onions and he's never had a wife;
Nor anybody else's – he lives just like a monk.
Religiously each Friday he gets rolling drunk.

And when the inn has closed I will weave my way back home,
Full of the joys of spring and singing loudly out of tune.
And if you should see me standing behind some old tree trunk,
I'm simply letting steam off, 'cos I'm rolling drunk.

The Roughton Wriggle Song

I gave my love a ri-ing, that had no stones;
I gave my love a cherry, that had no bones;
I gave my love a chi-ick, with no cry in;
I gave my love a baby, that had no end.

How can there be a ri-ing, that has no stones?
How can there be a cherry, that has no bones?
How can there be a chi-ick, with no cry in?
How can there be a baby, that has no end?

A ring when it's a signet, it has no stone;
And any bloomin' cherry, it has no bone;
A chick, when it is strangled, has no cry in;
Of babies, you'll agree-ee, there is no end.

But signets, by bird watchers, are often ringed;
And chi-icks on a Friday are often stoned –
They make no bones about it, drinking cherry bee,
And often end up having a little ba-by.

(The last verse of this song was collected by Dave Burland from a Barnsley version.)

This is a song I only do with my Partner in Crime, Dave Burland. You have to sing it with another person or you get stuck after verse one, because you've got no one to ask you the questions in verse two. I mean, you couldn't very well ask yourself, could you, because if you did you'd look a fool when it came to verse three and it become obvious that you knew the answers all along. Mind you, he surprised me by coming up with a fourth verse what gives more answers to the answers! That's how they are in his village of Barnsley, apparently – they won't take yes for a question.

A wriggle is a sort of silly question which you get a silly answer to, like 'What's got three legs but is always legless?' The answer to that is 'Nothing.' It used to be 'Albert Kipper', but since Albert died the wriggle don't work no more. Most of them don't work anyhow, because they never explain how the gooseberry got in the lift in the first place, never mind how it reached up to press the buttons. So all in all wriggles are just a way of making nonsense and if you ask me there's plenty enough of that about already, thank you.

Shepherd of the Ups

Tandouri

I'm a shepherd of the Ups, I have yows and hogs and tups, There are shear-lings too and weth-ers that I keep. I have flee-cy lit-tle lambs, two great en-or-mous rams, And some-times I may al-so herd some sheep. Oh I rise up at Dawn, she's the fair-est ev-er born, But then I must be-gin the dail-y slog; I will first brew up me tea, then sing all up the lea, And mer-ri-ly I'll whist-le, up me dog.

I'm a shepherd of the Ups, I have yows and hogs and tups,
There are shearlings too and wethers that I keep.
I have fleecy little lambs, two great enormous rams,
And sometimes I may also herd some sheep.
Oh I rise up at Dawn, she's the fairest ever born,
But then I must begin the daily slog;
I will first brew up me tea, then sing all up the lea,
And merrily I'll whistle, up me dog.

All day I keep my bunch of Kents and Suffolk Punch,
Of Yorkies, and Red Leicester Guernsey ewes;
For in the end I find that it makes but little mind –
They're all very much alike in mutton stew.
Now a shepherd must keep watch not to lose one of his flock,
And with the greatest care I count my sheep,
I count them by the score, and I count them all once more,
Then with all that counting sheep I fall asleep.

Well as the day declines I will wake midst columbines,
With parsley, sage and thyme, and rosemaree;
If you want to be perverse you may say the shepherd's purse,
But Perse looks after pigs – the shepherd's me.
When the dark begins to creep I will fold my little sheep,
For always I'm afraid they'll come to harm;
I fold them very neat, tuck in their little feet,
And stack them up all tidy in the barn.

This song is from the Norfolk Ups – especially Northrups and Southrups – where the highest point is 194 feet, which means that if you got up a stepladder you could be over 200 feet high! Not that anyone from Norfolk would do that, 'cos they'd probably get dizzy and fall off! Of course, we don't get a lot of sheep about our way these days, 'cos we found out what was causing them, but years ago they was a proper menace. It all come about when they had what they called 'the disclosures', where they fenced off the land and kept sheep to graze it. Anyone who've got a lawn will understand. The problem is keeping the grass down. Now some of these rich folk had hundreds of acres, plus no end of rods, poles and perches, and so on, and it all had to be kept down. What they discovered was that sheep could graze the grass just as well as peasants, with the added bonuses that you got the wool and they din't tend to set fire to your hayricks, or get with child by you and insist on maintenance. Well, even if they did, a lamb don't take a lot of maintaining anyhow. So they threw the people out and got sheep instead.

The word sheep come from an old word 'shep', which meant a sheep dog. So a Downs Ewe is, properly speaking, a Down Shep. But there's not just the one sort of sheep – there's lots of sorts. Some of them you probably know, like roast lamb with rosemary, mutton stew, lack of ram, and such. But there's also specialist sorts. There's Wendesleydales for cheese, Dorsets for people in Dorset I suppose, Border and Cotswold for morris dancing, Marinos for people at the seaside, and so on. As well as them you've also got what they call the 'rare breeds'. They're called that because they very rarely – well, you know, they have a lot of headaches. I expect their heads get too hot with all that wool being pulled over their eyes. But once upon a time these rare breeds were only rare in particular places – like the places they din't come from. You see, all different parts of the country were proud of having their own sorts of sheep and in those particular parts they were common as mud.

My old Uncle Walter once had a sheep. He reckoned there was never a dull moment. There's dipping them, combing their wool, lambing – all sorts of stuff. Of course, in Australia they do things upside down – I know that 'cos I had a relative went to Australia. That was Bruce Kipper. He was a very famous man. He was the only person ever to be transported to Australia and then transported back again by the Australians! He was in a sheep-shearing gang, which used to maraude around the backout, shearing people's sheep before they had a chance to stop them and then making off with the fleeces.

Of course, in Norfolk, we do things right way up and sheep shearing was done in a sort of a closed shop. Now closed shops are terrible things – especially if you happen to run out of fags on a Sunday afternoon. Apparently they used to shear the sheep in closed shops so that only the people they wanted to could have a go. There used to be people banging away on their knockers, wanting to have a go at some shearing, but all to know of ale – which always remind me of my Uncle George, 'cos he used to know of ale. He knew far too much of ale according to Aunt Ruby. Anyhow, the thing I'm trying to get at is that not just any old Tom, Thumb or Harriet was allowed to do the sheep shearing

If you want to know more about this sort of thing you ought to watch that telly programme 'One Man and his Dog'. Robin Page, who foreworded me is in that (although, properly speaking, as it has more sheep than dogs, and lots of people, it should be called 'Several People and their Sheep'). Otherwise just get on and sing the song.

The Song of the F.U.

Al Gore

Come all you bold young farmers, this message ne'er forget; Though you are strong, un-i-ted we will be strong-er yet. If we stand firm to-geth-er we soon will have our way; Lon-ger hours for low-er wag-es, with short-er hol-i-days. Join the Far-mers Un-ion, join the fa-voured few; Let our cry go yon-der; 'We are the great F. U.'

Come all you bold young farmers, this message ne'er forget:
Though you are strong, united we will be stronger yet.
If we stand firm together we soon will have our way:
Longer hours for lower wages, with shorter holidays.

Chorus
Join the Farmers' Union, join the favoured few;
Let our cry go yonder: 'We are the great F.U.'

The workers are ungrateful for all that we provide –
If we give them bread they ask for jam on it besides;
If we give them water, why then they call for ale,
And if we give them four good walls they want a roof as well.

God made us low and highly, God made us poor and rich;
The farmer in his farmhouse, the poor man in his ditch.
For we are all his children, the greatest and the least;
The working man is equal to any other beast.

The labourer needs labour, for idle hands will stray;
The master needs his mistresses, lest he be all work, no play.
The peasants are revolting, but this word to them we send:
Drop your combinations and reveal your wicked ends!

The Stick of Rhubarb

Al dente

Come all you fair and ten-der men, I pray be al-ways on your guard; Be-e-ware, be-ware, to-o keep your gar-den fair, And let no-one ste-al you rhu-barb.

Come all you fair and tender men,
I pray be always on your guard;
Beware, beware, to keep your garden fair,
And let no one steal your rhubarb.

Chorus
For rhubarb is a precious thing;
Rhubarb means all to a man.
O-oh rhubarb in it's season
Can drive away all reason,
And when pulled it will surely come again.

The gardener she was standing by;
I told her I'd like it in a tart.
She promised she would take it, and all in her oven
bake it,
But she said it must grow more e'er she'd start.

Now I put my rhubarb all on show:
The judges said they'd mark my card.
Oh I won a special prize at the North Walsham
assize;
Now my rhubarb is in for twelve months hard.

In April my rhubarb springs to life;
It swells most splendidly in May;
It flourishes in June and is eagerly consumed,
But in Julie it withers clean away.

This is one of them really old and mysterious songs that nobody have the first idea what it's about. You see, with these really old songs it's all a lot of symbolics. Take that one that goes 'Are you going to Narborough Fair, Wormwood, gall and turpentine?' – what's that all about? Or that other one: 'The trees they do go high' – do that really mean the trees get smelly? Nobody knows. The only thing you might notice is they all have something to do with plants. But it don't really matter, 'cos, like I said, its all a lot of symbolics.

So why do people go on singing songs when they don't know what they're about? I mean, you might as well hog the whole go and do world music in foreign languages – at least then you'd know that you din't know what it meant. Mind you, I reckon there's a lot to be said for world music. I mean, if you forget the words nobody need ever be the wiser – and you can wear interesting costumes without having to take up morris dancing. You don't even have to sing in tune.

But no. You see, this is good old British stuff that no one understands. It's part of our heritage. So it's our duty to look after it and hand it on to the next generation, so they can be as ignorant as we are. The only thing you can be sure about with this sort of thing is that they're never about what they say they're about. So this song have nothing to do with rhubarb.

Those in Peril on the Land

Matelot

Come list-en how this sail-or boy was cru-e-ly be-calmed, When I went with that Gun-ton girl she rolled me in her arms; She twirled me in her legs, oh and she whirled me in her hands; Well I woke up sore lam-en-ting, and in per-il on the land. In per-il on the land; in per-il on the land; I woke up sore lam-en-ting, and in per-il on the land.

Come listen how this sailor boy was cruelly becalmed,
When I went with that Gunton girl, she rolled me in her arms,
She twirled me in her legs, oh and she whirled me in her hands;
Well I woke up sore lamenting, and in peril on the land.

Chorus
In peril on the land; in peril on the land.
I woke up sore lamenting, and in peril on the land.

Them Gunton girls they scupper you, for when you fall asleep
They wash and press your jacket blue, they fetch you food to eat;
Hide money 'neath your pillow, put a gold ring on your hand,
But when they fetch the parson you're in peril on the land.

When first I tried land-lubbing life I thought it quite the thing;
Oh her father was a farmer, so I went and worked for him.
But backing up the cart one day I saw the mistress stand –
When I cried 'Avast behind' I was in peril on the land.

The mistress told the master, and the master told his wife,
And when she told my missus, well she caused to me great strife;
For it's love the girls and leave them – that suits a sailor man –
But, alas, you must stay with them when in peril on the land.

So come all you gallant sailor boys, don't run away from sea,
And never you let a Gunton girl an inch above your knee;
For if you do she'll grapple you, she'll board hand over hand,
And soon you will be pressed by her, in peril on the land.

This song is about being guntoned. You see, the young women of Gunton at one time got fed up with having all their young men shanghied and made to go to sea, so they started guntoning: they got hold of passing sailors, and made them stay on land. There they had to suffer terrible softships like lying on feather beds, sleeping all night, having decent food, and so on. But there was nothing they could do about it, because they'd taken the King's florin. What they used to do was leave the florin on the floor in the gents' lavatory in the Nelson's Arm, then when the sailors picked it up they said they'd taken it and that was a contract. That was a bit like when they used to put a shilling in the bottom of their drink, so when they drunk it by accident they was signed up for the navy. Only of course a florin outbid a shilling.

The song comes from my great uncle, Albert Kipper. He was a sailor, as you'd have known if you ever met him, because he'd have told you. Plus, he also had a wooden leg. He used it for things like nailing up boxes and playing snooker. We never found out whose it was, as a matter of fact, but he always had it with him. Quite often he used to wear it. He was the original one when they say someone waltzed into the room. He could really do it!

Albert Kipper (centre) wearing his wooden leg.

Times of the Rigs

This song was written by my Uncle George, who do a lot of song writing. But he's not as well known for it as he might be. That's mainly because he's not free to go round exposing himself. He's not free to go round doing anything, as a matter of fact. It all goes back to 1984, when he went to help the police with their inquiries. They found him so helpful that they gave him a full-time position in the Isle of Wight.

When they started with the North Sea oil that was like a sort of gold rush – except it was for oil, of course. A lot of people thought they'd be able to put out in their boats and fish some oil out of the sea, but, of course, they couldn't. Not then. Now they can, though, due to all these tankers having oil leaks. I had one of them on my Zodiac once, but in them days people thought nothing of it. I mean, in them days an oiled sea bird was a WREN who'd had a few. We used too keep a sharp eye out for them and if we saw one we called the RSPCA – that was because Percy Spratt worked for them, and he had a thing about uniforms. Now my Uncle George have a thing about uniforms, but there's nothing he can do about it.

There's strange things afoot down at Yarmouth,
And I don't mean the Isle of Wight!
'Cos they reckon there aren't no more herring,
And the mackerel, and haddock won't bite.
Now me father was fishing before me,
And me mother was in the marines,
So when they told me there was money in oil
I thought they were talking sardines.

Chorus
Whack all the day, diddle all the day,
Whack all the day and diddle all the day;
Whack all the day, diddle all the day,
Whack and diddle all the day, I do.

But one day I was lying down below,
Just sucking on a fisherman's friend,
When the mate cried out 'Slick off the port bow.'
Well I come quick, as you may depend.
'Three sheets to the wind,' I commanded,
'Turn the capstan full strength to the rear;
Splice the main brace, whack the diddle in place,
And stand by to haul out your gear.'

Well I put me glass eye in me eye glass
And I felt the warm wind on me cheek;
I hoist me son over the yard arm,
And up on that slick we did sneak.
We drifted, we trawled and we longlined,
We baited our hooks, and our breath;
But each time we thought we had it high and dry
We saw it was still low and wet.

All night we struggled to land it,
But it beat us, whatever we tried.
So I lit my old pipe while I pondered,
And flicked the match over the side.
And blast, when they said there was money
In oil, well they sure never lied:
We was blown back to port in ten seconds short,
With a deck full of fish, ready fried!

We Will Rob You

Breakingandentri

All you gee - zers sweet - ly sleep, do not stir, We will nick your coats of fur. We will rob you, rob you, rob you; We will rob you, rob you, rob you; You hang stock -ings on your beds; We wear ours up - on or heads.

All you geezers sweetly sleep, do not stir,
We will nick your coats of fur.
We will rob you, rob you, rob you;
We will rob you, rob you, rob you;
You hang stocking on your beds;
We wear ours upon our heads.

For our little babies' sake, do not wake;
Christmas is a time to take.
We will rob you, rob you, rob you;
We will rob you, rob you, rob you;
Charity begins at home –
Your home is the one we've chose.

While you dream of wise men three, bearing gifts,
Myrrh and frankincense to sniff,
We will rob you, rob you, rob you;
We will rob you, rob you, rob you;
You can keep the smelly stuff;
Gold is good enough for us.

You may toss and turn at night, for you know,
Rich men can't to heaven go.
We will rob you, rob you, rob you;
We will rob you, rob you, rob you;
Now you can sleep sweet for you're
Not a rich man any more.

Last year at about this time, we got nicked,
I got nine months, he got six.
We will rob you, rob you, rob you;
We will rob you, rob you, rob you;
That's the reason why, we fear,
We can come but once a year.

Where Have All the Cauliflowers Gone?

Eve-ry-bod-y brings their har-vest home, Eve-ry-bod-y that you know; The
cab-bage patch brings just as much pride As the farm-er's sway-ing set-a-side.
God gives us the weeds so high, And the cab-bage white but-ter-fly, So let us give
thanks to God, For what we get from the sod.

Everybody brings their harvest home,
Everybody that you know;
The cabbage patch brings just as much pride
As the farmer's swaying set-aside.
God gives us the weeds so high,
And the cabbage white butterfly,
So let us give thanks to God,
For what we get from the sod.

Everybody brings their harvest home,
Everybody that you know;
Even the strumpet on the game,
Brings her harvest home the same.
God gives us the strumpet – well –
You have to pay, so I've heard tell;
Personally I don't know:
My wife wouldn't let me bring one home.

Everybody brings their harvest home,
Everybody that you know;
From the scrubber, scrubbing on her knees,
To the policeman, bringing home the thieves.

God gives us the thieves, it's true,
So when they steal your things from you
You're helping, with the things you own,
Them to bring their harvest home.

Everybody bring their harvest home,
Everybody that you know;
Except for the welder, who welds so hard,
Leaves his harvest at the shipyard.
God gives us the welder fair,
But still he leaves his harvest there,
For his wife would give him gyp
If he brought home a blooming great ship.

Everybody brings their harvest home,
Everybody that you know;
All you people had to pay,
So I'll take my harvest home today.
God gave me this song, you see,
So, if it's rubbish, don't blame me;
Everybody brings their harvest home,
As I think my song has shown –
So I'll just say 'Cheerio.'

The Wraggle-Taggle Travellers-Oh

There were three travellers, all in a van, and the van was old and weary-oh;
And it broke down on John Lord's land, so there camped the wraggle-taggle travellers-oh.

John Lord came home all on a Monday, and he called out for his Tracy-oh;
Her mum said 'She's been gone two days, all along with the wraggle-taggle travellers-oh.'

'Then fetch to me my trusty steed, oh bring to me my Harley-oh.'
'Oh fetch it yourself and now I see why she's gone with the wraggle-taggle travellers -oh.'

Well he got out his trusty steed, and he rode off from the bungalow;
And off he rode till his wife he seed, all along with the wraggle-taggle travellers-oh.

Oh he called out to his own wedded wife, 'That's typical of a Scorpio;
How could you leave your comfortable life, just to go with the wraggle-taggle travellers-oh?'

'Well what care I for your continental quilt, your foot spa and jacuseeo?
For I will lay on the dewy, dewy ground, all along with me wraggle-taggle traveller-oh.'

'Oh what has he to give to you – with his little penny whistle-oh?'
'Oh no penny whistle but a digereedoo, has my own wraggle-taggle traveller-oh.'

'No bolognaise then will you scoff, no quiche and no pistachio –
No Mateus Rosé will you quoff, all along with your wraggle-taggle travellers-oh.'

'All from the hedgerow I will dine, on hips and haws and mistletoe,
And Watney's Red shall be my wine, all along with the wraggle-taggle travellers-oh.'

And then he said these words of fate: 'Oh I have set the video
For seven thirty until eight' – and she looked at the wraggle-taggle travellers-oh.

Then to John's pillion she did leap and she has called out 'Cheerio';
For when it comes to Coronation Street, well, bugger the wraggle-taggle travellers-oh.

This is the last song in the book, due to it still being in pathetic order. This is one of the really old songs. It's exactly how my grandfather Billy Kipper used to sing it. Except that my Uncle George brought it up to date in 1972. Which means, of course, it's out of date again, now.

George did it because he found old folk-songs could be dangerous. I'll tell you how that come about. One day he come to a mossy bank and he decided to throw this young maiden down on it, like they do in all the best folk-songs. Well, as it happened, she weren't too pleased and she told her mother. Her mother said if George thought he could go round throwing young maidens down on mossy banks then he'd got another think coming and she give George a thick lug. She give the young maiden one too, for good measure (which in them days was in feet and inches). So when her mother had gone the young maiden give George a thick lugful and all in all George decided that old folk-songs could be dangerous, like I said. In the end he also discovered the girl weren't no maiden either, but that's another story. So George decided to bring some of the old folk-songs up to date for safety's sake, but mostly they never caught on. There was things like 'I've Lost My Spotted Dick', 'Twankydildo' and 'The Lincolnshire Embezzler', but this is the only one what really survived.

This was Billy Kipper's special bath song. It was only ever sung when he had his bath, which was always on a Saturday. As a matter of fact it was the third Saturday in August. Now Grandfather's bath was quite an event. The whole house used to get into a roar-up beforehand. Well, first off we had to find where we'd put the bath when he'd finished with it last year. Then grandmother had to make a flannel out of some old underthings and someone had to go round the village to try and borrow some soap, and so on. Then, come the day, we all prayed for good weather. You see, Billy always had his bath out in the orchard, 'cos he reckoned that bathing indoors was unhygienic. So everyone had to heat up water in anything that come to hand and then that all had to be hauled out to the orchard. Finally, when he was sure that the water was the right temperature, and he had his decoy duck to play with, and the wind was in the right direction, and so on, he went inside this sort of screene-off area we made with old tilts, and got into the bath. And then he started to sing this song.

But one year that was most especially exciting. You see, Billy had this thing about folk-song correctors like Cecil Sharphouse and William Vaughan-Ralph, and them. No matter how they begged he wouldn't let them have any of his songs. But this particular year, just before what they called the Great War, they come to hear about his singing in the bath. So when word got round that his bath was coming up they hid up the trees in the orchard overnight with their notebooks. And when he started to sing they whipped out their pencils and notebooks – though some of them had pens – to write down the song. Of course they fell out of the trees, due to having nothing to hang on with. So, soon after Billy started singing, these correctors started dropping out of the trees like windfalls and the dogs chased them, and they lost their notebooks. That was great fun. And, at the end of the day, grandfather was clean, the correctors was gone, and we had all these new songs from their notebooks to sing.

In fact, I reckon some of them must be some of the songs in this book. Well, I know some of them are. This one is, actually. You see, when he looked through those notebooks he found they had a better version of this song than he did, so he started doing that instead. And, just to rub it in, he sent them his version to replace it. So all the versions of this song you find in other books are actually Billy's version, which he got rid of. But this was his proper old special bath song – after 1913 it was, anyhow. And that's long ago enough for anyone I should have thought.

The Kipper Family Up the Ages

To understand Sid Kipper's unique standing as a singer and player of English song it's necessary to realise that he is only the latest in a long line of Kippers. In fact he can trace his ancestry back to Boadikippa, the famous Queen of the Iceni, who fought against the Romans.

> She was also very popular for setting fire to Colchester and inventing the combine harvester. But the Iceni didn't just kill people – sometimes they maimed them first. They was also very musical. Nowadays you don't hear much Icenic music, due to the fact that the Iceni all done the decent thing and got killed. Not like the Celts. They all buggered off west. Well, we've got long memories in Norfolk. We haven't forgotten. We can forgive them for the buggering off. What we can't forgive them for is the buggering back again with their blooming Celtic music.

Sid now leads the Icenic Music movement. He has revived a variety of Iceni instruments, such as the English Bodhran and the Norfolk Small Organ.

> The musicians always led the troops into the battle, in order to make their sinews stiff. They reckon the sight of them coming at you with their Small Organs was enough to stiffen anybody. The only trouble was, if they lost the battle, that was very difficult running away with their instruments, 'cos they used to trip up on their tubing. So the musicians was the first to be wiped out in fact.

After the Iceni were defeated by the Romans one of Boadikippa's sons became leader of what was left of the tribe. He was Ethelkippa, also known as Eric the Red Herring or, more often, Eric the Kipper (supposedly because he was two-faced and gutless).

> I'm a direct descendant of Boadikippa herself. Of course, that doesn't make me king of Trunch or nothing. As a matter of fact the one what have the best claim to the throne is Tracy, who do the hairdressing about the village. So if you ever hear of Colchester being set fire to again you'll know who to blame.

And so the Kipper line continued down the years, connecting Sid directly to such worthies as Canute Kipper, who was tragically drowned, Ferdinand Kipper, the first man to circumnavigate Gimingham, and so on. And, of course, to their music. So when Sid sings the songs in this book he is uniquely informed by a living link to the past from which they came. It's what makes his singing so powerful, so authoritative and so out of date.

VERSE THREE – THE MORAL

*In which our hero tells strange tales, puts on his parts,
and dances off playing his nuts.*

From what has gone before the reader might have received the impression that Sid's sole contribution to the folk arts has been his singing. That would be a grave error. So, in order to reflect the wider aspects of Sid's repertoire, this section of the book contains a glimpse of some of his other activities. There's a piece about playing the walnut-shells, instructions for a dance, traditional drama, and, first and foremost, some of Sid's vast treasury of stories – because Sid's reputation for tale-telling is now nearly as great as that for his singing.

Story-telling has one great advantage – unlike folk-singing you can get Arts Council Grants for it. The Arts establishment think the only real sort of singing is not that of their native land, but the imported singing of opera. Hence, all the grants for singing go to opera and none to folk-song. So I have encouraged Sid to develop this side of his repertoire in the hope that we might be able to attract some of those grants.

Of course, these stories are part of an aural tradition and consequently vary from time to time. However, I have taken the liberty of writing them down, based on a number of tellings from Sid. I have also taken the liberty of putting them into something approximating to English.

The Story of Saint Nick of Trunch

Saint Nick, the patron saint of burglars, started off as Just Plane Nick. He was called Just Plane because he came from St Just, which is in the flat part of Norfolk. Now being a burglar isn't easy in the flat part of Norfolk, because people can see you coming from a long way off. They can see you going from a long way off too. Consequently poor old Plane Nick had to do his business when people was otherwise detained – otherwise he might have been detained himself!

Now, the only night he could be sure of being safe was Christmas Eve. On Christmas Eve everyone was distracted. They was all busy scrubbing behind their various bits and pieces because their in-laws would be coming to Christmas dinner the next day, whether they liked it or not. So, on Christmas Eve, Nick would set out with his sack which had the letters S.W.A.G. written on it – well, he'd nicked it from the Swaffield Women's Anti-crime Group. Now, when he was working, he always wore a red, fur-trimmed coat, with a hood, a big white beard and a pillow up his jumper. That was his disguise. At least, that's what he said. I mean, it wasn't much of a disguise, because as soon as anyone saw it they said 'Oh look, there's Nick dressed for work – it must be Christmas Eve, then.'

Now, in them days, burglars used to specialise – that way the police knew who done what, so that was alright. Nick, for instance, had his own way of breaking in, which was to come down the chimney. And he only ever took two things – mince pies, and sherry. So, on Christmas Eve, people used to put the fire out, and leave mince pies and sherry for him. That way they saved themselves the trouble of having him poking around in their drawers – with his clothes on fire.

But this is the story of how he become Saint Nick. Well, it all happened one year when these new people moved into the village and invited all their friends round for a traditional country Christmas. Come the Christmas Eve, Nick set off on his rounds. In due time he come to the new people's house and that's when the trouble started. You see they was as ignorant as sin. They didn't know nothing about traditional country Christmases. They hadn't put out no mince pies nor sherry, nor nothing. They hadn't put the fire out, either! So when Plane Nick went down the chimney he had a nasty surprise. So did they, when he landed in their grate all black and smoking, and swearing fit to print. Well, they panicked. They all ran out of the house, shouting and screaming. Some said as how the house was haunted. And some said it was Old Nick himself, come to get them. And some said that was what happened when you moved to places what din't have no culture. And they ran and ran, and were never seen again.

Well, the traditional country villagers all cheered. They said good riddance. They said as how Nick ought to be a Saint for the driving out of them people. And so, from then on, he was always known as Saint Nick. And when he died they wanted to bury him in the church, but there was some dispute over whether he was a proper saint or not. So they did the next best thing. They buried him up the vicarage chimney.

And that's why, on Christmas Eve, people leave out mince pies, and sherry in the memory of Saint Nick. And that's why, no matter how he tries, the vicar can never get a decent fire going.

The Case of the Cuckoo's Nest

This is an even older story than the previous one, and is brimming over with symbolism and imagery. Versions have been found as far afield as Knapton and Gimingham, so it's rather surprising that it was overlooked by the Grim Brothers when they published their 'Grim Fairy Tales' in 1812.

Once upon a time there was a princess who was pure as the driven snow and as beautiful as a turkey – which is a compliment where I come from! Howsomever, she was wholly fed up. You see, four and twenty handsome princes wanted to marry her. Well, four weren't too bad, but the other twenty was a real pain. They used to hang about the palace all day, getting under foot. She couldn't even get no peace at night, 'cos there'd always be princes climbing up the ivy and banging about her secret passage. It all got on her beautiful wick. So she went for a walk in the woods, and she decided that the only solution was to marry one of the princes, just to get rid of the other four and nineteen. But which one should she marry? Of course, they were all handsome and rich, but looks and money aren't everything (personally I'd settle for either, but this is a fairy story). She decided to set them a quest, to see which of them was worthy of her beautiful hand. Just as she'd decided this she met a wrinkled old crone and she confined in her. The old crone cackled, like they do, and she said 'Tell them to bring you the cuckoo's nest, my dear.' So she went back and told the handsome princes and they all rode off to look for the cuckoo's nest. And life became much better for the Princess. There was no one hiding under her fifteen mattresses, nobody drinking champagne from her slippers and making them all soggy. Lovely.

And three long years passed. No, I tell a lie, because two of the years was just the usual length. But one of them was a leap year, so one long year and two ordinary ones passed, and one by one the princes got fed up, and give up the quest. All except for Prince Nigel, who truly loved the princess. He was as pure as she was and determined to win her beautiful heart – as well as all the other bits of her. He searched high and he searched wide. He searched far and he searched low. He searched day in and night out, but he couldn't find no cuckoo's nest. Then, one day, he met a wrinkled old crone in the woods and he confined in her.

'Well,' she cackled, 'as a matter of fact I've got a cuckoo's nest. But if you want it you must sleep with me.'

'Good idea,' he say. 'What with all this searching night and wide I could do with a bit of kip.'

'Well,' she say, 'when I say "sleep" I don't mean sleep as such. I mean you must satisfy my bodily lusts.' Well he weren't exactly sure what they were, being so pure, but he said 'fair enough'. So he lay down with her and after she'd showed him what to do, he took to it like a duck to orange sauce. And the next morning he awoke to see, there on the pillow beside him, was the wrinkled old crone, grinning like hell.

Well, to cut a long story short, she give him the cuckoo's nest, he rode off, high and wide, night and low, far and day, come to the palace, give it to the princess, they got married, and went to the bedroom – which is where it get interesting again! When she stood there without a stitch to her name, her beauty was enough to strike a pure man speechless. So he said 'Your breasts are like the ripest pomegranates; your belly, that's like a dew-kissed melon; your loins – your loins are like one of those rude-looking parsnips you sometimes get.'

'All very well,' she say, 'but I'm so pure I don't know what they're for – at least if they was fruit and veg you could eat them.'

Then how he blessed the wrinkled old crone who had showed him what to do. And by the end of that night the princess decided that handsome princes weren't totally useless after all. And just nine months later they had a little Princelet. But strangely enough it din't look like the handsome prince and it didn't look like the beautiful princess. In fact, it bore a striking resemblance to the wrinkled old crone. And it grew up, and made their lives a misery ever after.

How the Turkey Got His Gobble

Normally with traditional material the author is unknown. However, the name of Rudyard Kipper is always associated with this tale and the others like it, which are known collectively as 'The St Just So Stories'. Rudyard was also a poet, perhaps best known for his poem 'If Not', in which a young man is told that success in life lies in doing what the others do – 'if not' a number of uncomfortable things will happen. It has been the inspiration of many generations of Truncheons.

A long time ago, oh best belovéd – when the world was young and the Broads were narrow – there was a big, sad bird called the turkey. He was called the turkey because he came from the South of America – which is just below where the Indians come from and just above where the penguins are wrapped. He was sad because, although he was a big bird and a feathery bird, and although he lived in the county of Norfolk (where men were men, and women wished they weren't), he din't have no mating call. He could whistle like a blackbird, but he was too big for that. He could roar like a lion, but he was too beaky for that. He could sing like a whale, but he was too dry for that. And one day, oh best bewildered, he stood amidst the reeds and grasses of the great, grey, greasy River Stiff, and he felt the mating season come on. So he waggled his wattle and he opened his beak to call for a mate. First he whistled like a blackbird, but that only attracted female blackbirds. Then he roared like a lion, but that only attracted lionesses. Then he sang like a whale, but that only attracted a lot of whaler-men. And no matter what he did, oh best bedevilled, he couldn't attract what he wanted. He couldn't attract female turkeys.

So the turkey went to see the very wise and wisdommed old owl. The owl had a call of his own – to whit, that is to say, a hoot.

'Give me your hoot,' said the turkey, 'so that I may have a voice of my own and call for a mate.'

But the owl was too old and too wisdommed for that. 'Oh, terrible turkey,' he said, 'that cannot be, for it is the owl that hoots for a mate, just as it is the pigeon that coos for a mate and the rabbit that seems to manage fine without any sort of a call whatsoever.'

'Then tell me, Oh owlish one,' said the turkey, 'if the pigeon coos and the rabbit seems to manage fine without any sort of a call whatsoever, then what is it that the turkey does?'

'The turkey,' said the wise, wisdommed old owl, 'seems to me to be doomed to do without.' And the turkey, oh best befuddled, was most terrible angry. And he stamped his foot. And he stiffened his feathers. And he threw back his head and he let out a great wail of frustration. But just then, oh best bereaved, a bumbling bee was flying overhead. And the bumbling bee, as you know, was a great thinker. Just at that moment he was thinking about flying. He thought and he thought, and he thought that really, all things considered, it shouldn't be possible for bumbling bees to fly. And he lost faith in himself and he fell from the sky – straight into the turkey's mouth, and on to his tonsils. And the turkey, oh best bedraggled, began to gobble. It tried to blow the bumbling bee out, but it was too big. It tried to swallow the bumbling bee in, but it was too small. And the turkey looked around for help, and he saw lots and lots of female turkeys, come to see who could be making such a racket.

And from that day to this, oh best beheaded, the turkey has gobbled, the female turkeys have come to see, and the bumbling bee has decided that thinking is not all it's cracked up to be! So when you gobble your Christmas dinner this year, remember this – a turkey is just for Christmas, not for life.

The Horrible History of the *Harry Celeste*

Albert Kipper, from whom this story comes, died in 1951 – not 1926, as stated in the book *Prewd and Prejudice*. Which would be obvious to anyone who knew him – especially in the years between 1926 and 1951. Or anyone who read *Prewd and Prejudice*, come to that, since it say there as how he was playing cricket in 1931! Anyhow, this is a true story about what happened to my Uncle Albert, told to me one dark and stormy night as he dandled me on his knee. That was in 1951, as a matter of fact. Of course, when he told it he din't do what I do and say that it happened to his Uncle Albert. First off he din't have no Uncle Albert, and second off it wouldn't have been true even if he had, because it didn't happen to him. Especially as he din't exist. That's how these stories change over the years, due to people not having Uncle Alberts who weren't there when it happened anyhow!

It all happened one dark, foggy night at sea. And the person it happened to was my Great Uncle Albert Kipper. Young Albert, as he was then called (although later in life he changed his name to old Albert) was serving as a deck-hand on the *Harry Celeste*, which was a sort of brother ship to the *Marie Celeste*. Now being a deck-hand weren't bad going, 'cos he'd only started a year before as ship's cat, so he was doing pretty well.

The *Harry Celeste* was really a sort of opposite to the *Marie Celeste*. I don't know if you know that story, but on the *Marie Celeste* they found all the tables nicely laid, but there was nobody there to eat it. Well, on the *Harry Celeste* there was loads of people who wanted to eat it, but no bugger wanted to lay the table! The *Harry Celeste* put out from Yarmouth with a cargo of coal, bound for Newcastle. Now that weren't easy sailing in them days, because you was at the mercy of the winds and the tides. Plus, you was also at the mercy of the ship's officers, who weren't up to a lot. You see half of them were young blokes who had been sent off to sea by their fathers, for falling in love with unsuitable young women. And the other half were unsuitable young women, dressed up as men, going after them. So all in all they din't know enough about ships to make a pair of sailor's trousers.

Anyhow, on this particular night they were becalmed off Scratby, in a terrible fog. Night after night she lay there in that fog. Night after night there was no breath of a wind. Night after night there was not a sound to be heard. What happened during the days I don't know, because Albert was on permanent nights. That was his job to sit up for'ard and sound the fog horn every five minutes. So, for hour after hour, Albert honked into the fog, but answer came there none.

Then, all of a sudden, a strange ship hoved slowly into view and Albert felt his face go white, and he heard his flesh creep. The ship that was hoving into view was in a terrible state: the rigging was all torn and the sheets hadn't been changed for weeks; there was seaweed growing on it, and it shone all over with a ghastly hue (which is not to be confused with Ghastly Hugh who used to live in Gimingham: he didn't shine at all).

Anyhow, this ship come hoving closer and closer, and closer still, until Albert was sure there'd be a collision – and if he was any judge that'd be between the two ships. He was so frightened that he couldn't bear to look. So we'll never know what happened!

Which isn't much of an ending, but that's as far as Albert got before I got fed up with being dandled, poked him in the eye and he fell off the chair. He died in the sidecar on the way to the hospital, without finishing the story. Bloody inconsiderate I call it.

Prewd and Prejudice
by Chris Sugden and Sid Kipper

Sid's biggest story-telling venture, one in which I accompanied him, led to the publication, in 1994, of the book *Prewd and Prejudice*. This publishing millstone was greeted with much acclaim:

Jim Lloyd, on Radio 2's 'Folk on 2', said: 'A fascinating addition to the genre of country journals.'

The Guardian said: 'A belated satire on *The Country Diary of an Edwardian Lady*: the snobbish Miriam Prewd stays in the Norfolk village of St Just-near-Trunch, tormented by the oafish, inbred, pagan locals. I make no claims for this as licherchur, but there are half-a-dozen good throwaway jokes per page. Best read drunk.'

Sid Kipper says: 'I never found nothing fascinating about addition – nor subtraction, neither, come to that. And fancy them calling the Old Goat Inn an oafish, inbred, pagan local! If they're so clever then how come they can't even spell liquorice? As to that about being best read drunk – well, how do they think it was written?'

To date the book has been reprinted twice so I say that readers can make up their own minds on the matter by buying at least one copy of the book, details of which can be found at the end of this volume.

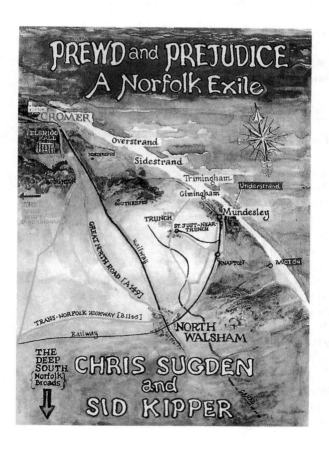

The Trunch Nightsoilmen's Play

An often neglected part of the English folk tradition is its drama. Yet at one time the streets of our towns and villages were full of mummers, mystery players, pace-eggers, and the like. The plays were commonly performed and handed on by a particular trade – for instance, *The Grocer's Play*. In Trunch, however, *The Grocer's Play* has not survived well, since the village eventually had only one grocer, making it more like a grocer's monologue. St Just's premier play was *The Nightsoilmen's Play*. It had various forms, depending on how many nightsoilmen were available, but here is one of the more frequently performed versions.

Enter the mummers, singing a song:

> Here we come this morning or afternoon, or night –
> Delete as appropriate – to bring to you delight.
> We are jolly mummers, so pay to us good heed,
> While we with our mumming do merrily proceed:

All   Mum mum mum mum etc.

M. C.   I am Mother Christymas and I come here today
With all of these fine heroes, before you all to play;
There have been rehearsals for weeks and weeks on end –
A shame then that none of us could actually attend!

All   Mum mum mum mum etc.

Geo.   My name it is George and I am a bold Knight,
I come here today for to look for a fight.
I'm no good at cooking or at cricket or at chess,
But at killing, and maiming I am simply the best.

All   Mum mum mum mum etc.

B. A.   My name is Bold Aroma, the Turkish Nightsoilman,
I travel far, I travel wide, just for to fill my can.
Good fresh fertiliser is always in great need
And any contributions will be gratefully received.

All   Mum mum mum mum etc.

M. C.   In comes I, Mother Christmas,
Dressed in all that gleams and glisters.
Our tale is full of lust and wit,
As well as all the usual bits.
My part's not big, but as they say –
Size isn't important anyway.

Geo.   In comes I, George is my name,
A hero bold of famous fame.
My fame is famous – I'm not just braggin' –

I've killed the damsel and rescued the dragon!
I've met the Frog, the Turk, the Hun
And massacred each, and every one.
So to anyone it's plain as paint
That I should be a holy saint.
But when I sent off to apply
They said that first I have to die!
To be *Saint* George is my desire
So quickly now I must expire.
But seeing as suicide won't do,
I'll pick a fight, and bravely lose.

Come on then – who'll fight George of famous fame – whose fame is famous?

B. A.   In comes I, Bold Aroma,
My smell is known from York to Cromer.
My trade is vital to women and men,
But somehow I've not made many friends.
I'm not bitter – I'm stout, but mild,
Fighting is by me reviled.
Peace and love are my delight –
I never, ever, ever fight.

Because nothing was ever settled by fighting.

Geo.   What about the wars in France?

B. A.   Well, apart from them.

M. C.   And the wars in Germany?

B. A.   And those, I suppose.

Geo.   And boxing matches?

B. A.   Don't think I don't know your desire:
You hope this way to raise my fire.
But that won't work at all, I fear –
It's not been raised in many's the year.
We are all brothers beneath the skin:
Bob's your Auntie and mine's a gin.
Do what you will, 'twill not avail,
To make me fight you'll surely fail.

Geo.   What if I was just to attack you?

B. A.   Oh, well, that's different. Go on then, try it.

Geo.   Oh yeah?

B. A.   Yeah!

(They grapple – B. A. forces George back with his stomach.)

Geo.   No – I've gone off the idea

(George turns away and B. A. fells him from behind.)

B. A.   He who lives by the sword shall die by the brush.

Geo.   Out goes I, *Saint* George.

M. C.   Is there a doctor in the house?

Inc.   In come I.

M. C.   In come you, who?

Inc.   Yoo-hoo!

M. C.   Who are you that comes in?

Inc.   In comes I, an incomer.
             I first came here on my hols last summer.
             I fell for the place all in a trice;
             I mean country life is just so nice.
             But what's this (Looks at Nightsoilman.) – there's a funny smell –
             And this man (Looks at George.) doesn't seem too well.

M. C.   Are you a doctor?

Inc.   Well, no, but still I shall not shirk –
             I've done a bit of social work.
             (To George) Just come along now my good feller –
             Why don't you pull yourself together?

             (George gets fed up, rises and becomes the doctor.)

Doc.   In comes I, a doctor most able,
             I've studied my books and learned all my tables.
             I can square the hypotenuse and decline the verb –
             In fact my credentials are quite superb.

B. A.   Doctor, this man …(Stops as he realises there is no body.)

M. C.   Is there a body in the house?

(They recruit the Incomer as the body.)

B. A.   Doctor, this man has the gout and the ague,
         The pox and the palsy, the pester, and plague you;
         He has ingrowing toe-nails and out-growing toes;
         A frog in his throat and a pea up his nose.
         In fact, he is an ex-George; he has turned up his toes; he has gone to meet his maker;
         He is pining for the fjords ...

M. C.   Stop making it up as you go along – have you no respect for the tradition?

Doc.   If all the facts are as you have said,
         It's my firm opinion – he's probably dead.

B. A.   Your diagnosis is quick and sure;
         Come then – be as deft with the cure.

Doc.   The cure? It's no good you asking me.
         I am a doctor of philosophy.
         But this is a riddle – when we say George is dead,
         What do we mean by what we have said?
         Some would say that his mind isn't present –
         He doesn't think, therefore he isn't.
         But here he is, large as life, on the floor –
         And, besides, he didn't think much before.
         Others might argue that his soul has departed,
         But his soles and his heels are just where they started.
         To clear up this riddle is clearly my duty;
         Ipso facto and et tu Brute.
         If the difference between life and death we can't name,
         Then quid pro quo rata, they must both be the same.

B. A.   If that's the conclusion at which you arrive,
         Then it seems to me he must still be alive!

(George rises from the dead.)

Doc.   A miracle – who said philosophy's no practical use.
         He'll live to fight another day –
         He's not a Catholic anyway.

M. C.   So our play is ended, there's just one more thing –
         To prove it's all over, the fat man must sing.

Doc.   I thought I was singing?

B. A.   You are!

83

Tess of the Baskervilles
by Augustus Swineherd

Those who have seen Sid performing in such dramatic masterpieces as *Snow White and the Seven Deadly Sins* or *The Trunch Nightsoilman's Play* will realise that he has considerable talent in that direction. Sid's first major role, apart from playing the back end of the pantomime donkey in *Big Dick Whittington*, was in Swineherd's epic mystery, *Tess of the Baskervilles*. Here is part of that great work.

Somewhere, out in the Great Gimingham Mire, was the hound. I, Doc Watson, troubleshooter for the property firm, Sherlock Homes, was engaged to get rid of it. But it wasn't proving easy. When I served an eviction order on it, it just licked me. When I tried to chase it off it barked, ran away and brought me a stick. I remembered my old friend saying 'It's all to do with the dog that barked in the night.'
　　'But the dog didn't bark in the night,' I protested.
　　'Exactly,' he said, sniffing opium from his slipper. 'Find out when the dog did bark and you'll have the answer.'
　　'But how could that help? This damned dog barks all the time.'
　　But events took a strange turn when Sir Huge O'Baskerville set off across the Mire to seek out a young woman.

Sir Huge:　(Calling) Tess. Tess. I know you're there girl. You must come out and take your medicine.

Tess:　I'm not on the medicine no more. They all cleared up after Granny Gimlet put a charm on them. 'You don't want to take no more of that old medicine,' she said. 'Let old Granny charm them away.' And she did too – they vanished like a maiden's honour in a squire's bedroom.

Sir Huge:　Tess, you cannot stay here. You are putting yourself in mortal danger. You do not know who you are.

Tess:　That's just what Granny Gimlet used to say. 'None of us know who we really are,' she said, just before she accidentally turned herself into a frog. Who am I then?

Sir Huge:　You are Tess of the Baskervilles and there is a terrible curse upon you! A dreadful fate threatens you! It's a horrible secret!

Tess:　Why don't you ever look on the bright side? There you go on about everything being terrible and dreadful, and horrible as if nothing nice ever happened. Why, just this afternoon I trod in some sheep's droppings and that's ever such good luck, Granny used to say. 'Course, she'll never do that again – though she might hop into some. I don't know if that's lucky or not.

Sir Huge:　Cease your prattle. I must have you off my land this minute.

Tess:　Oh, you are a hound Sir Baskerville. But I don't see how that's possible. Your land stretches for miles around here. If you want to have me this minute it'll have to be on your land. Of course, if you could hold yourself in for a bit that might be different.

Sir Huge:	If you stay on Baskerville soil this night you will never see the dawn. For do you not know what night it is?
Tess:	Don't tell me – let me guess. It's Walperverts' Night. No? Is it All Heels' Eve? No? I give in then – though the bit about your land still applies.
Sir Huge:	Tess, tonight is the anniversary of the night you were born. On this night, seventeen long years ago, Betsy, the milkmaid, spent many painful hours in labour. She sweated and screamed, and called out for deliverance. Then, when she'd finished her work, she was allowed to give birth to you. My father, Sir Jasper O'Baskerville, was furious. He confessed that he had laid with Betsy – although he claimed that he never inhaled. He admitted that you were the fruit of his loins. And then he swore that you should never thrive. He swore that he would have his revenge on himself for his wicked doings. He swore that the Great Gimingham Mire would have you before your eighteenth birthday.
Tess:	Swore a lot, didn't he? And him all landed, and all. Granny Gimlet always said that people who swore a lot only showed that they didn't have a big enough thingy.
Sir Huge:	Thingy? How dare you impugn my father's thingy!
Tess:	Not thingy – *thingy*. You know. Like all the words you know.
Sir Huge:	You mean vocabulary?
Tess:	That's it. Granny said that people who swear a lot don't have a big enough one of them.

And then they heard a terrible sound. It was a sort of a moaning, some would say. Others would call it more of a howling. Yet others wouldn't come down on one side or the other.

Tess:	Oh, Sir Huge, what is it?
Sir Huge:	Oh no. No, it can't be. It couldn't be. See – it isn't!

What was it then? Was it the cause of all that moaning? What will become of poor Tess? We may never know the answers to these rhetorical questions, for at this very point Augustus Swineherd had to leave for a darts match, where he was tragically wounded by a dart through the eye, and couldn't see his way to finishing the story. Nevertheless Sid's performance in this play was agreed by all to be a triumph. It is said that his portrayal of Tess brought a tear to many an eye and a lump to many a throat.

The Trimmingham Triangular Six

This dance is included for those interested in such things. Sid occasionally does some dance calling, delighting dancers with his extensive knowledge of the Trunch tradition. It is yet another string to his bow.

Mind you, I can't see how you could fire a bow with more than one string. But what people don't know is that these old country dances always used to tell a story. Dances like the Gimingham Gay Gordons and the Cromer Clap Dance was all about particular things – although in those two cases I'd rather not say what the particular things are. In fact the first one is about being particular in a particular sort of way and the second one is about not being particular enough!

    Anyhow, this dance tells the story of the Infernal Triangle, which is where one person wants another person, but the other person wants another other person, while the other other person wants the one person in the first place, who doesn't want them. This leads to a lot of confusion. Well, no one knows whether they're the one person, the other person or the other other person. In the end they all usually give up and stick to the person they started with because at least they know who they are. And that's the story of this dance.

(Tune: - 'The Downs and Ups')

86

Instructions

Formation

Form triangular sets, with three couples per set, men with their partners on their right (this represents the Infernal Triangle).

Figure 1 – 'unlucky seven'

Take right hands with your partner, then pass them and dance round the set twice, taking alternate hands with the people you meet, counting up to seven – this should be your partner again. As you meet your partner start to go past them, but don't let go hands and pull them back (this represents trying to get away from your partner, but not succeeding).

Figure 2 – 'balance and swing'

Facing your partner, step to alternate sides twice, starting left, as if trying to get past them. Repeat another twice whilst swinging a punch with the fist on the same side as you are stepping (this represents the couple falling out – it is sometimes also known as a 'rant').

Figure 3 – 'having a fling'

Turn away from your partner – you are now facing another person, who is your 'bit on the side'. Dance around and about them, with your arms in the air, shouting 'yee-haw' or 'way-hay' (this symbolises the partners having a bit of a fling with their bits on the side).

Figure 4 – 'community charge'

Take your 'bit on the side' in a ballroom hold and charge off across the room. Turn as a couple, then charge back to reform the set (this symbolises going off for a bit with your bit on the side).

Then

Start again with your 'bit on the side' as your new partner. Dance the dance three or six times through, so you end up with the partner you first started with (this represents the total futility of the whole business).

Sid calls a dance with the Albion Dance Band.

Sid Kipper's Walnut-shell Workshop

Having included something to delight singers, story- tellers and dancers, I will end with something which will have musicians swooning. At last Sid has agreed to reveal the secrets of the instrument for which he is most especially renowned – the walnut-shells. Anyone who has seen Sid beat pulsing rhythms as he whirls them around his head will no doubt be inspired to put down this book and grab their own.

Starting from Basics – Four Steps to Success with the Walnuts

Step 1: If you really want to start off from the basics you'd better plant a walnut and then find something else to do for twenty years while you wait for it to grow. Otherwise you ought to just nick some walnuts from Mrs Dace's Corner Shop like what I do.

Step 2: Get a walnut knife, stick it in your walnut and split it in two. Scrape out the nut and eat it, 'cos this'll help you keep going. Keep on splitting nuts till you get two pairs of whole halves.

Step 3a: Now you need a drill and the drill is this: bore a couple of holes in each shell, thread some knicker elastic through, and tie it so the shells fit on your thumbs and middle fingers.

Step 3b: Now check to see that you've done step 3a so the open part of the shell is outwards – if not start again (though you don't have to plant a new tree).

Step 4: There is no step 4. The four steps are step 1, step 2, step 3a and step 3b - can't you count? If you need any more steps you'll have to start with step 1 again. If not, you're ready to learn to play your nuts.

Carrying on from Basics

Some Simple Exercises: Do 50 star jumps, 20 press ups and go for a run round the village. That won't help with playing the nuts 'cos you'll be too knackered, but that's up to you. Otherwise ignore this bit.

Tone: Start by banging the shells together and trying to get a good tone. You'll know when you get it because people will stop saying 'For goodness sake stop that bloody awful row, you've got a terrible tone', and they'll just say 'For goodness sake stop that bloody awful row' instead.

Rhythm: Once you've got tone you can have a go at rhythm. The walnut-shells will play any rhythm you like, plus some you won't like, but the best sort to start off with are the World Music ones. With them you can play any old sort of rhythm and people will still think you're a clever clogs. Then you can work up to something really difficult like a waltz.

Style: Style is the most important thing of all. Of course if you're playing on the wireless or for a load of blind people it don't matter, but if people can see you then it does. I don't want to get personal, but style is really a personal thing. So we'll say no more about it.

Seven Things You Didn't Really Want to Know about the Walnut-shells

1. Castanets is Spanish for chestnut. Now this just shows how daft foreigners are, 'cos chestnuts don't have two halves, so you can't bang them together – and if you could they'd just fall apart, and you'd be left with knicker elastic round your fingers, which isn't always a good thing.

2. The chorus of 'The Nutting Boy' goes:
> When he asked her to go with him she always answered nay,
> But when she saw his nuts so trim she could not him gainsay.

3. The second Wednesday in Lent was known round my parts as Walnut Wednesday, because 'On this day no walnut shall be eaten or beaten.' The punishment was to drink five pints of beer against your will, whether you liked it or not. This was a very popular custom.

4. You mainly get the walnut shells in the south bit of England. This is mainly due to walnuts not growing very well up the north, which is why they had to invent bagpipes instead.

5. You don't need to read music to play the walnut shells. The traditional thing is to write 'Start banging' and 'Stop banging.' There are diagrams for those what can't read.

6. In America the walnut is called the Shagbark. They're worse than the Spanish if you ask me.

7. The Trunch Walnut Dancers can be seen dancing through the street of St Just-near-Trunch at midnight on May 1st. Well, they can only be heard, as a matter of fact, since the bulb in the street lamp broke. Still, they're a breath-taking sound, as they whirl and leap in their traditional walnut costumes.

Choice and Care of the Nuts

You should always have a good pair of nuts available. English ones can be too soft and Californian ones are too brittle, so I always use the Chinese ones, mainly because that's what Mrs Dace has in her shop. And you should always look after your nuts. After playing you should give them a good wipe down with some walnut oil. This helps keep them in good nick. And if you look after your nuts they should give satisfaction for many years to come.

Sid demonstrates the Gimingham Grip.

Chris Sugden and Sid Kipper – A Joint Statement on their Behalf

Some people have expressed an unwarranted interest in our exact relationship. They are aware that we have business connections and that we write together, yet they remark that we are rarely, if ever, seen together. They note that Chris has somehow obtained copyright to all of Sid's songs and wonder if the talented country boy is being exploited by the urbane wheeler-dealer.

We would like hereby to state that we are both fully satisfied with our current arrangements and join together in condemning such unnecessary intrusion. However, in order to dispel any further speculation, we are prepared to reinstate, at this point, a part of the biography which had been edited out at an earlier stage.

Gutted

January 1993 was a crucial month for Sid and I. I was living in Norwich, which to Sid was the Big City. He was gradually finding the hustle and bustle of metropolitan life more exciting than St Just, and was coming into Norwich more and more for the night life, at places like the Denmark Arms, where the 'sessions' were renown, and, it was said, they opened you with welcome arms. Unfortunately the last train in the direction of Trunch left long before closing time, so Sid took to sleeping on my floor.

'Course, there was a spare bed, but somehow when you're in the Big City that seem more exciting to sleep on the floor. Anyhow, when you've picked the lock on Sugden's drinks cupboard it's easier to stay where you fall than get up and look for a bedroom.

Things came to a head when Sid suggested that, since he was at my house so often, it would be more convenient if he moved his ferrets in.

Well, they was pining for me. They're one-person carnivores are ferrets and mother couldn't cope with them. Well, actually, they couldn't cope with mother either – not many people can. Anyhow, when I brought them up on the train to Sugden's I found he'd moved. And he'd taken the drinks cupboard, too. That weren't for weeks till I found out he wasn't paying the rent no more. Nor the gas and electric. When they come round for the money that was a bit embarrassing – well, I was in bed with a roadie at the time. So I had to pack up my ferrets and go home.

This was the start of Sid taking more responsibility for his own affairs. He moved back home to St Just, where he still lives to this day, and I moved to Yorkshire. Now we communicate mainly through third parties such as his agents, publisher, and so on. We get on much better that way, and as long as he doesn't find out where I'm living there's no reason why we shouldn't go on working apart for years.

We trust that this will stop any further speculation regarding our relationship and conclude by stating unequivocally that we are not even good friends.

Chris Sugden

Sid Kipper

In an unconsciously ironic post-modern gesture Sid manipulates a dancing doll which bears a striking resemblance to his own father, thus exposing a triad of contradictions: the retired man dances yet; the grown son dandles the baby father on his knee; the child stabs the adult in the back. The word redolent springs to mind.

This picture encapsulates the Trunch Tradition. Through the songs and stories in this book it has become apparent that old Kippers never die – they always leave a lingering whiff of themselves which, try as you might, cannot be expunged. No doubt Sid Kipper will, in his turn, leave behind his own essence – indeed, many people say that he already does.

The most exciting thing of all is that the end of this book is not the end of the story. The ballad of Sid Kipper goes on, and who knows what new verses are yet to be added? Only time will tell. Indeed, it is with some trepidation that I conclude this book with the words:

To be continued...

FURTHER READING -- AND LISTENING

BOOKS

Prewd and Prejudice by Chris Sugden and Sid Kipper
Published by Mousehold Press, 1994 (ISBN 1 874739 03 X).
The story of Mrs Miriam Prewd's stay in the village of St Just-near-Trunch in 1904 and 1905.

Since Time Immoral (The Kipper Family Songbook)
Published By EFDSS, 1986 (ISBN 0 85418 149 O).
The early songs of the Kipper Family, reproduced from Billy Kipper's old bluesongbook.

RECORDINGS

Sid Kipper – Like a Rhinestone Cowboy (1993), Leader Records, LER 2115.
Sid's solo album, featuring many of the songs in this book.

The Kipper Family – In the Family Way (1991), Dambuster Records, DAM 023.
Henry's retirement party, featuring all the family, including George, Len and Annie, with archive contributions from Albert, Billy, and Jimmy.

The Kipper Family – Arrest these Merry Gentlemen (1989), Dambuster Records, DAM 022.
Christmas capers, with a healthy seasoning of Rev. Derek Bream and a touch of Kevin Kipper.

The Kipper Family – Fresh Yesterday (1988), Dambuster Records, DAM 020.
Recorded live in Trunch Village Hall.

The Kipper Family introduce The Crab Wars (1986), Dambuster Records, DAM 017.
A mighty Ballad Opera, originally a double album, telling the story that hadn't been told for 300 years. Featuring the likes of Martin 'Watersons' Carthy, John 'Richard Thompson Band' Kirkpatrick, Phil 'Show of Hands' Beer and Cathy 'Fiddlers Dram' Lesurf.

The Kipper Family – The Ever Decreasing Circle (1985), Dambuster Records, DAM 012.
Songs of the seasons with the inestimable accompaniment of the New Trunch Coronation Band.

The Kipper Family – Since Time Immoral (1984), Dambuster Records, DAM 005.
The album that launched the Kipper Family on an unsuspecting public, to great acclaim.

LIVE PERFORMANCES

The Sid Kipper Mailing List sends out details of Sid's appearances, products, and so on, about four times a year. If you would like to be put on the list simply send your full name and address to 10 Perseverance Road, Mountain, Queensbury, Bradford, BD13 1LY.

A brief and very basic tape of only the tunes to the songs in this book is available, featuring just one verse (and chorus where appropriate) of each song. The cost is £2.50 (including post and packaging) from the address above.

THE COUNTRYSIDE RESTORATION TRUST

The Countryside Restoration Trust has become Sid's adopted charity. The Trust (of which Robin Page is Chairman) is working towards the co-existence of farming with wildlife and attractive landscapes. For further details write to:

The Countryside Restoration Trust,
Barton,
Cambridgeshire, CB3 7AG.

INDEX of SONGS